PERILS OF EATING POISON-ANIMAL

How Eating Pork Destroys The Eater

Kevin A. Muhammad

TechDoc, Incorporated
Newark, Delaware

Perils of Eating Poison-Animal: How Eating Pork Destroys The Eater

Published in the United States by:
TechDoc, Incorporated
35 Stature Drive
Newark, Delaware 19713
www.etechpublish.com

Printed in the United States of America.

Main entry under title:
Perils of Eating Poison-Animal: How Eating Pork Destroys The Eater

A TechDoc, Incorporated book
Bibliography: p.224, graphics, tables

Library of Congress Card No. 2005909090
ISBN: 0-9658864-3-3

Cover designed by Dreu Pennington-McNeil

Dedication

To the members of the human family who seek to know and learn of the correct diet for humans; and who are in pursuit of optimum health and longevity. This book is a testimony of that Guidance — *How To Eat To Live, (books 1 & 2),* written by the Honorable Elijah Muhammad.

Special Thanks

All Praise and Honor Belongs to Almighty Allah (God), Who Came in the Person of Master Fard Muhammad, the Great Mahdi, for Giving Humanity Divine Guides in the Persons of the Honorable Elijah Muhammad and the Honorable Minister Louis Farrakhan.

I thank my beloved wife, Marcia, for the time and energy in editing this book; my son, Kevin, Jr., for helping me with the research; my daughter, Krystina, for her inspiration; my mother, Helen Owens, for keeping me grounded in Christ; my twin brother, Julian Muhammad, for his generosity and inspiration. Their great love and support made this effort possible.

I thank Sis. Dreu Pennington-McNeil for the cover design; and Bro. Anthony X Irvin, Sis. Siddeeqah Muhammad and Bro. Willie F.X. Scott for proofreading this text. I thank Sis. Judy Muhammad for her continuous encouragement, love and support.

I thank Bro. Minister Robert Muhammad, the Believers of Muhammad Mosque No. 35, and all those wonderful souls who helped to make this book possible.

Words of Wisdom

Please, for our health's sake, stop eating it; for our beauty's sake, stop eating it; for our obedience to God and His Laws against this flesh, stop eating it; for a long life, stop eating it; and for the sake of modesty, stop eating it.

— *from the Honorable Elijah Muhammad, Book 2 of How To Eat To Live*

Books By Kevin A. Muhammad

Obesity, Diabetes and How To Eat To Live, Second Edition

Nuts Are Not Good for Humans: Biological Consequences of Consumption

The Slave Diet, Disease & Reparations

FAQs about How To Eat To Live, Volume One

FAQs about How To Eat To Live, Volume Two

Peril —

n 1: a source of danger; a possibility of incurring loss or misfortune; "drinking alcohol is a health hazard" [syn: hazard, jeopardy, risk] 2: a state of danger involving risk [syn: riskiness] 3: a venture undertaken without regard to possible loss or injury; "he saw the rewards but not the risks of crime"; "there was a danger he would do the wrong thing" [syn: risk, danger] v 1: pose a threat to; present a danger to; "The pollution is endangering the crops" [syn: endanger, jeopardize, menace, threaten, imperil] 2: put in a dangerous, disadvantageous, or difficult position [syn: queer, expose, scupper, endanger]

PREFACE

The following words by the Honorable Elijah Muhammad inspired this work:

"I will be a happy man when I see the day that our Black people forsake the hog."

This statement moved me in a way that I cannot fully express in the confines of this text. I thought deeply about the heart of a man that desires his people to discard this divinely-forbidden and extremely unhealthy meat from their diets. Most fascinating to me is how this simple admonishment – forsaking swine – is an awesome demonstration of *divine love*.

The Honorable Elijah Muhammad has placed this same love in those who, under the leadership of the Honorable Minister Louis Farrakhan, strive to follow Him as redeemers and healers of an abandoned and broken people, the Black man and woman of America, as well as the human family, in general.

This divine love, as well as my desire to see the Honorable Elijah Muhammad happy through our achievement of this noble objective, fueled my effort to write this book.

The goal of this book, *Perils of Eating Poison-Animal*, is to educate the reader about the diseased nature of swine by pinpointing the virulent pathogens that persist in this animal, and by showing the enormity of the diseases incurred by those who eat this flesh.

In ensuring the success of this goal, I chose to mount this subject on the Divine Revelation from Almighty Allah, in the Person of Master Fard Muhammad, which HE revealed to the Honorable Elijah Muhammad. More specifically, *The Problem Book* of *The Supreme Wisdom* is the cornerstone of this book, as it identifies the root of Black America's social, health, and economic problems and provides us with the insight and guidance to solve them.

PERILS OF EATING POISON-ANIMAL

Contents

INTRODUCTION

Key Terms: *Black America.* This term, used throughout this book, refers to the enslaved Black people of America, who continue to practice a culture that has its origin in the chattel slavery era, which has made us victims of disease and early mortality.

This World. This term, used throughout this book, refers to the current world system, which is characterized by injustice, inequality, warmongering, an inordinate quest for profit at the expense of human life; disrespect of human life and rejection of divine laws and guidance — the world of Satan.

S wine has been a chief meat in the diet of Black America. The legacy of eating this poisonous flesh has its roots in the chattel slavery era when we were forced-fed this meat for nearly four centuries.

Epidemiological studies regarding the health plight of Black people in America reveal that we are beset with many infectious and chronic diseases. This has been a four-hundred year old saga, and our poor dietary practices have been the only consistent reason given for this national crisis.

Those who write these studies postulate that certain nutrients must be added to our diets, while other nutrients must be reduced if we are to achieve better health. This approach has proved very confusing and contradictory, which is consistent with the way of a world driven by greed. These studies are no more than mere facades to keep the public from realizing that all guidance from *this world's* institutions lead to disappointment, disease and death — profit centers of this world. There is not any wonder why the health plight of Black people persists.

The Supreme Being, Master Fard Muhammad, gave the solution to our problems, which HE conveyed through the Honorable Elijah Muhammad. An aspect of this simple solution is: *there are things that should be thrown out of our diets, and there are foods that should be added to our diets.* The focus is on foods and not on nutrients, because all foods contain nutrients. Also, we do not eat individual nutrients, we eat foods.

First up, are the things that must be eliminated from our diets. Why? In following the bestial practices of our enslavers we eat as they eat — anything and everything, living or dead, helpful and harmful. Therefore, the foods that injure us must be identified first. This, too, must be done according to priority. The highest priority is obedience to God, for adherence to HIS food laws must come first, and not obedience to government agencies that sanction and promote the use of drugs and alcohol, and the consumption of poisonous foods.

In this pool of forbidden foods, the flesh of the swine is the most urgent to eliminate from our diets. Why? Violation of this law sentences the violator to banishment from God's favor and rejection from HIS kingdom. This is confirmed in the Scriptures of the Holy Quran and Bible.

MOUNTING DIVINE REVELATION
. . . .

In the *Problem Book*, which is one of the Lessons of *The Supreme Wisdom* given by Master Fard Muhammad to the Honorable Elijah Muhammad, the pitiful state of Black America is described. The unlabeled introduction of this book reads:

> This Book teaches the Lost-Found Nation of Islam a thorough knowledge of our miserable state of condition in a mathematical way when we were found by Our Saviour, W. D. Fard.

These words are loaded with great significance, and each of us can attest to the fact that we, Black America, have many deeply rooted problems that make our existence miserable. This makes the quality of our lives seem as though there is "no" quality at all.

Miserable is described:

> Very uncomfortable or unhappy; wretched; causing or accompanied by great discomfort or distress; mean or shameful or contemptible; wretchedly inadequate; and; of poor quality, inferior.

There is no doubt that these words describe the pre- and post-slavery conditions of Black people. Who can deny that the state of Black America has been woeful since we were emancipated? This is verified in every report – issued since that time – that assessed our health status.

HONORABLE ELIJAH MUHAMMAD

Honorable Elijah Muhammad received the divine revelation from Master Fard Muhammad and began teaching civilization to the enslaved Black People of America.

Returning to the introduction of *The Problem Book*, the *mathematical way* is the precise cause of our problems and the precise solutions to correct them. It stands to reason that if Almighty God identified the problems and provided us with the solutions, then our success is contingent upon how well we implement these solutions. We must act from HIS guidance to achieve success.

For far too long, we have adopted *this world's* view of our problems and how we should solve them, and because this world lacks the love of Black people, and many people profit from our suffering, these so-called efforts are inherently bogus. To believe that this world's healthcare industry wants to improve Black people's health is the same as believing that wolves want sheep to enjoy long lives. It is not in the nature of the wolf to want such a thing.

Just the same, it is not in the hearts of those who control America to want the best for Black people. This is why our disastrous health condition remains the same, and has worsened, despite all the alleged attempts to solve it.

BOOK'S FOUNDATION

The foundation of this book is *Problem 9* of *The Problem Book* in *The Supreme Wisdom*. Master Fard Muhammad writes:

> The population of Detroit is one million five hundred thousand people, and there are two hundred and fifty thousand original nation. During these hard times for the lack of jobs, not having enough money to buy food, they eat two meals per day.

> Suppose the average person eats four ounces of bread, ten and one-fifth ounces of poison-animal, three and one-third ounces of rice, four and one-eighth ounces of other meal helper. It is known to the Medical Profession and other wise Muslim Sons that poison-animal sounds the mental power; one-sixtieth of an ounce per every ten ounces of poison-animal.

> If the average person contains seven and one-half ounces of brain, then Mr. Muhammad wants to know how long will it take to sound the seven and one-half ounces at the above eating rates. The average person can be robbed successfully with one-third of unsound brain. Then how long will a Devil have to wait to rob of said, the poison-animal eater, at the above rates?

> It is also known to the civilized world that ten ounces of the poison animal destroys three one-hundredths percent of the beauty of a person. Then Mr. Muhammad wants to know how long will it take to destroy the whole, one hundred percent of the beauty appearance at the above eating rates?

The consequences of eating this divinely-prohibited flesh are very clear. The beauty and brains of the swine eater are destroyed at calculable rates. These destructive workings should be of interest to everyone, particularly at a time when people are doing just about anything to hold on to their youth and beauty. The swine eater loses both at an accelerated pace.

The mind of the swine eater is also destroyed at an accelerated rate, yet few people care about or are aware of this destruction. Many people spend billions of dollars on surgical procedures, potions, and chemical injections in an attempt to maintain their beauty. However, beauty is destroyed from within, particularly by eating foods that injure the cells and tissues of the body. These external efforts, although costly, are useless if we continue to eat poisonous foods.

Obeying the divine law prohibiting the eating and touching of swine saves us from the harsh physiological degeneration caused by the pathogens contained in swine. The Honorable Elijah Muhammad states that eating swine can be the cause of the diseases and ailments we suffer. Consequently, these ailments lead to early mortality. Through it all, the pathogens are the cause of death, and not diabetes or heart disease that manifest from pathogenic infections.

THIS BOOK'S CONTENT

Following are brief overviews of the chapters contained in this book.

CHAPTER 1: DYSFUNCTIONAL CULTURAL HABITS

Black America's social, economic, and health plights are not new realities. They are legacies arising from our continued bondage in North America. This chapter provides a historical background of how pork entered the diet of Black America, and the health plight caused by "dysfunctional cultural habits" rooted in the chattel slavery era.

CHAPTER 2: SWINE AND DIVINE LAW

Swine flesh is now the meat of choice among many nations. Some of these nations profess to be committed to religious beliefs; however, adherence to divine law is absent these commitments. This chapter addresses *this world's* political and religious standings regarding the domestic and worldwide consumption of swine — in the context of Divine Law. We answer the most valuable, yet often overlooked, question: *Why does God forbid us to eat swine?*

CHAPTER 3: WHY CALL IT POISON-ANIMAL

Swine flesh is called by many names, such as *pork* or *the other white meat*. These terms have roles in promoting the consumption of this meat. This chapter shows why Master Fard Muhammad used the term "poison animal" to refer to pork or swine flesh, and why this is the most appropriate noun for identifying this divinely-forbidden meat.

CHAPTER 4: POISONS IN POISON-ANIMAL

Just how poisonous is swine or poison-animal? Can these poisons really be eliminated by cooking this divinely-forbidden meat? This chapter discusses the poisonous nature of poison-animal and describes the most dangerous pathogens harbored in this flesh.

CHAPTER 5: TRICHINELLA INFESTATION

The Trichinella parasite holds a superior place among most helminthes and parasites. It is regarded as the "super" worm. This chapter describes the historical background, life cycle and overall pathology of the Trichinella parasite and shows why this parasite is the most formidable of all known poison-animal pathogens.

CHAPTER 6: PARASITIC PLUNDERING

What is the extent of the biological damage caused by parasitic infections? How many popular diseases, unbeknown to most people, are linked to parasites? This chapter describes the acute and chronic disease pathologies associated with poison-animal pathogens and how these conditions are connected with the current chronic disease pandemic.

CHAPTER 7: SOUNDING THE MENTAL POWER

Problem 9 of *The Problem Book*, in *The Supreme Wisdom*, describes the amount of poison-animal a person must eat to have his or her mental power sounded (brain damaged). This chapter describes how poison-animal pathogens destroy the brain of the poison-animal eater. It connects many common brain disorders to parasitic infections caused by poison-animal pathogens.

CHAPTER 8:...OR TOUCH THEIR CARCASSES

As with the overall global construct of farming practices, poison-animal farming is also a massive industrial enterprise. Much debate surrounds the enormous environmental destruction caused by these sadistic operations. This chapter describes the hellacious impact of industrial poison-animal farming on the environment and human life.

CHAPTER 9: CANNOT WALK UP TO THE STORE

Rheumatic diseases are the leading cause of chronic pain and disability. These conditions are pandemic in Black America. This chapter describes how poison-animal pathogens are responsible for many common rheumatic diseases, such as arthritis, gout, and lupus erythematosus.

CHAPTER 10: MOTHER TO CHILD

The way a mother lives before and during her pregnancy affects her unborn child in many ways. Her dietary habits are intrinsic to the child's mental and physical development. This chapter describes how poison-animal parasites, bacteria, viruses, and fungi are passed from the mother to the child – a process known as congenital infection – and the extraordinary health detriments that plague both mother and child.

CHAPTER 11: POISON-ANIMAL & DISUNITY

The quality of the food we eat has long been linked to how we think and behave. This chapter describes how eating poison-animal frustrates, impedes, and ultimately destroys the ability and willingness of Black people to unite. This is caused, in part, by the virulent pathogens that destroy the brain areas responsible for *reasoning* and *civil behavior*. Eating this meat is part of the broad scheme to keep Black people disunited.

DYSFUNCTIONAL CULTURAL HABITS

Throughout Our Sojourn

Key Terms: chronic disease, dietary trends, Federally-designated poverty line, Food-frequency questionnaire, hegemony, Industrial Revolution, morbidity, mortality, point-of-purchase, poison-animal, pork, Public Health Services Act, slavery, The Problem Book

According to a 1910 census report, Detroit's Black population – isolated in a section known as Black Bottom or Paradise Valley – numbered 5,741 and owned 25 businesses.[1] By 1920, the population had grown substantially and Black-owned businesses now numbered 350. These businesses included a movie theater, a pawn shop, a co-op grocery store and a bank. The Black community also had *17 physicians, 22 lawyers, 22 barber shops, 13 dentists, 12 cartage agencies, 11 tailors, 10 restaurants, 10 real estate dealers, eight grocers, six drug stores, five undertakers, four employment offices, and a few garages.*

The growth of Detroit's Black population was due to the rise of manufacturing industries in the northern states. The city was the benefactor of the Great Migration that began in the early 1900s. The impetus for this massive exodus of Black people from the South to the North included better economic opportunities and less racially-invasive bestial treatment than that experienced in the South. The opportunities were made available, in part, because of a decrease in the number of European immigrants — brought about by World War 1. The war kept Europeans anchored at home.

Just as Black people were used in the South to develop America's agricultural industry, we were now recruited by Northern Caucasians to serve as laborers during the Industrial Revolution.

Despite these so-called "better" conditions, such as increased wages, freedom of religious expression, and opportunities to service our own needs by establishing businesses, the evils of racism were widespread. Many of us lived in isolated, over-crowded, slum-like conditions that made us "easy pickings" for exploitative and abusive social and economic dealings.

For example, we still suffered economically by having to pay higher prices for rent, mortgages, insurance, food, medical treatment, and other goods and services. Mob attacks and police brutality were still huge factors in our overall distress and oppression. In short, the "North" was not the Promised Land.

BLACK BOTTOM DETROIT

Black Bottom residential street on the east side circa 1920.
The sign on the tree reads "Always Drive Safely."
(Courtesy of The Detroit News: Paradise Valley and Black Bottom by Vivian Baulch)

Many detrimental behaviors, resulting from centuries of enslavement, still remained. Ignorance about proper family relationships, proper diet, and community health were among these.

INGRAINED BEHAVIORS

The Honorable Elijah Muhammad pinpointed many self-defeating behaviors forced upon Black people during slavery. These behaviors were based on falsehoods and an atrociously foreign way of life. He identified our ignorance about God, self and others, and our poor dietary habits as the most paralyzing to us.

In the book, *Racism, Health, and Post-Industrialism,* the following gives the reason for the social scourges that persist in Black America:[2]

> In the context of cultural hegemony, dysfunctional cultural habits are very difficult to alter because they frequently are reinforced by the system of exploitation (especially if their continuation is in the interest of powerful elites) and become tied to the identity of the group, whose members now view such habits as traditional.

Black America's poor dietary practices are among the most important dysfunctional cultural habits that we have had difficulty altering for the better. These habits remain the chief cause of the astronomically high morbidity and mortality rates of Black America. During the early 1900s, we suffered greatly from heart disease, diabetes, cirrhosis, and cancer. Today, we still face the same conditions, and our overall health plight has worsened.

In *The Problem Book*, our Savior, Master Fard Muhammad, who appeared among us in 1930, in the Black Bottom section of Detroit, described the following in *Problem 9* of this Book:

> The population of Detroit is one million five hundred thousand people, and there are two hundred and fifty thousand original nation. During these hard times for the lack of jobs, not having enough money to buy food, they eat two meals per day.

> Supposed the average person eats four ounces of bread, ten and one-fifth ounces of poison animal, three and one-third ounces of rice, four and one-eighth ounces of other meal helper.

MASTER FARD MUHAMMAD

Master Fard Muhammad, The Great Mahdi, appeared among Black people in Black Bottom Detroit and began teaching us the knowledge of self and how to live supreme lifestyles.

Poison animal is pig, pork, hog, or the "other white meat". There is much in this; however, several things are obvious: 1) the Medical Profession knows that eating pork destroys the brain; 2) eating pork is part of the evil plan to continually rob the people; and, 3) Master Fard Muhammad identified the eating of pork as a major problem among Black people, HIS chosen people.

How did pork get into the diet of Black people? The Honorable Elijah Muhammad states that pork entered our diets during the chattel slavery era. History supports His words, as records show that pork fat and corn meal represented our core diet, while in slavery.

The book, *The Peculiar Institution*, provides a direct quote from Dr. John H. Wilson, a leading physician during the slave era.[3] He wrote the following in an 1859 essay on the proper feeding of "negro" slaves:

> How fortunate that pork and corn, the most valuable of all articles of diet for negroes, may be so readily produced throughout the whole region where slaves worked!

Both Caucasian plantation owners and physicians considered pork fat and corn as the healthiest food for the enslaved Black people. We were viewed in the same manner as livestock. The human factor, with respect to our existence, was totally absent.

On this same line, Dr. Wilson cautioned Caucasians about eating pork because eating it would cause them disease. During that time, medical thought sought to differentiate, physiologically, between Blacks and Caucasians. Generally, the things that were good for Caucasian people were often not good for Black people, and vice versa. No doubt, as the ruling group, Caucasians considered themselves superior; therefore, the best was for them, while the worst was suited for Blacks. The same sentiment continues today.

Some historians suggest that these recommendations made the *slaves...victims of ill-informed masters — of the primitive state of science and dietetics.*[3] This, of course, is an excuse. Clearly, the divine law of God forbidding the eating and touching of swine was known, particularly among those who claimed to be "good white Christians", which included many, if not all, slave owners.

Nonetheless, the damage was already done. This medical-sanction made pork the most dominant food in our diets. Our suffering was and remains immense.

According to *Problem 9*, Master Fard Muhammad found Black people – nearly 70 years up from chattel slavery – eating *ten and one-fifth ounces* of pork each day. Compared with the amount of the other items on the plate, pork still represented the greater portion of our meals. And, consequently, eating it kept us victims of disease.

SLAVE DIET PERSISTS

The research article, *Nutritional Assessment of a Predominantly African-American Inner-City Clinic Population*, reported the findings from a nutritional assessment of Black patients attending two inner-city health centers in Milwaukee, Wisconsin. At the time of the study, the two clinics, Martin Luther King Jr. Heritage Health Center, which has two locations; and Lisbon Community Health Clinic, served more than 14,000 low-income people — mostly Black people. The clinics serve an area that is a designated *health professional shortage area* (HPSA), which qualifies these institutions to receive federal funding.[4]

This majority Black population subsists in an economically blighted area. Approximately 40 percent of its residents have household incomes below the federally-designated poverty line. The researchers noted:

> In these neighborhoods, dilapidated housing, liquor stores, fast food restaurants, bars, and corner grocery stores abound.

Milwaukee is not alone. Today, the masses of Black people in America live under these conditions throughout American cities. These areas are isolated, blighted, and havens for broad exploitation of a people who have not rebounded from the horror of centuries of forced slavery and post-emancipation abuse.

According to the clinics' records, 81 percent of patients had incomes below the poverty line. Clinically, the general patient population had high incidences of obesity, diabetes, high blood pressure and heart disease. Given that the Martin Luther King Jr. Heritage Health Center, alone, has approximately 60,000 patient visits annually, these health conditions should be considered epidemic. However, federal and state health agencies rarely declare chronic diseases as epidemics or pandemics.

This study substantiated that, as is nationally suggested, Black people's diet is high in salt and fat, while lacking in fiber. Again, our poor dietary habits are intrinsically related to our disastrous health plight. The Honorable Elijah Muhammad said it best: *What you eat keeps you here and what you eat takes you away.*

The study, principally, featured two surveys. The first, a food-frequency questionnaire (FFQ), collected information about the foods the patients ate the previous day — the day before their visit to the clinic. Researchers believed that participants could easily recall what they ate the previous day, which would provide the highest chances for accuracy, as opposed to having to recollect an entire week.

Longer recall durations would have tainted the study because of the likelihood that participants would have guessed about what they ate during the week. These guesses, of course, would have reflected healthier diets, despite the fact that their health conditions showed otherwise.

Also, the logic in only requiring information about what the participants ate the prior evening or day was that these foods would most likely be the kinds of foods they eat throughout the week, month and year. Diet is an intrinsic part of a people's culture, so usually there are no significant deviations from the types of foods consumed. This fact validates the reason why the Black health crisis is very broad in scope.

In designing the FFQ, researchers chose to follow other studies, which suggested that whole milk, beef, eggs, butter, and cheese *contributed most to cholesterol/saturated fat intake independent of age, race, or sex*. This is debatable, as are most issues involving diet and nutrition.

Given that Black people consume 63 pounds of pork per person per year, compared to Caucasians at 49 pounds, and Hispanics at 45 pounds,[5] pork should have been included in the FFQ. In addition, pork fat and not beef fat is used in many traditional dishes that Black people eat. One wonders if omitting pork was deliberate, particularly when eating it produces far more health and social implications within a community than do beef or chicken consumption.

The second survey, completed by the grocery stores within this community, provided point-of-purchase data, which was used to determine the top selling food items. By using this particular survey, researchers could compare the participants' dietary intakes against the grocery store data to obtain a more accurate assessment of the community's overall consumption habits. The logic is that the food people buy is the food people eat.

Moreover, point-of-purchase data is particularly valuable in the *unique phenomenon of the corner store as a primary means for provision of groceries* to isolated populations. This data has high accuracy potential because people living in inner city communities do not grow their own food; and few of them have personal transportation to shop at suburban supermarkets.

The study featured surveys completed by 21 participants — 8 men and 13 women. Although this was a small population sample, the researchers believed that it reflected the majority of patients. This is a very realistic position, because families living in isolated communities are generational, and follow customs and traditions that make predispositions to diseases the norm.

All participants were clinically obese, and had substantially high intakes of fat and inadequate fiber intake. This was in keeping with Black America's historical dietary trends.

According to the assessment of the items listed on the survey, an average of 2,749 calories were consumed, with 42 and 14 percent being from fat and saturated fat, respectively. The most common items participants ate included butter, with an average weekly intake of 7 tablespoons, and beef at 3.38 servings per week. Fried chicken ranked third. Cheese, milk and butter contributed most to the saturated fat intake.

Twenty-two grocery stores completed the point-of-purchase survey. The predominant food items sold were chips, bologna, soft drinks, chicken wings, white bread, whole milk and Snickers. Frito-Lay *chips* were the most purchased food item.

The most significant sources of fat were bologna, hot dogs, bacon, chicken wings and pork chops. Although the researchers did not identify the type of meat of the bologna, bacon and hot dogs, we can strongly assume that it was pork. This being the case, four of these five items (chicken wings excluded) were poison-animal. In addition, the national average of 63 pounds of pork consumed by Black people confirms that pork must be a top selling meat in Black communities.

Comparing the FFQ data of the 21 participants to the grocery store data reveals significant gaps. Although beef and fried chicken were the dominant items in the previous meals, store data showed that pork products were the most sold items. Therefore, approximately 150 years up from chattel slavery, pork is a major meat in the diet of Black America.

The USDA's report, *Factors Affecting U.S. Pork Consumption*, revealed that Blacks eat approximately 63 pounds of pork per person per year compared to Caucasians at 49 pounds, and Hispanics at 45 pounds.[5] The report further detailed the following:

> Blacks ate almost 16 percent more processed pork and 58 percent more fresh pork than Whites. Among Blacks, processed pork was more popular than fresh pork (38 vs. 25 pounds)...Blacks ate more pork than other consumers and ate 82 percent of their total pork at home, compared with 76 percent for Whites.

This proves that pork is entrenched in Black America's diet, and establishes the fact that we continue to practice dietary habits associated with slavery. There is no doubt that this consumption habit is reinforced by the *system of exploitation*. By eating both fresh and processed pork products in abundance, we enable America's industrial swine industry to reap substantial profits.

If we compare this reality to our health plight, a line connecting the two is clearly drawn, prompting the question of how pork is involved in the obesity, diabetes, heart disease, and cancer epidemics. According to the report, *Health Disparities Experienced by Black or African Americans in the United States,*[6] Blacks experience a disproportionate burden of disease, injury, death, and disability.

The top three causes, as well as seven of the 10 leading causes of death, are the same for both Black and Caucasian people; however, the risk factors, incidence, morbidity, and mortality rates for these diseases and injuries are greater among Blacks. As of 2002, the top ten leading causes of mortality for Black people were: 1) diseases of the heart; 2) malignant neoplasms [cancer]; 3) cerebrovascular diseases; 4) Diabetes Mellitus; 5) unintentional injuries; 6) homicide; 7) Human immunodeficiency virus (HIV) disease; 8) chronic lower respiratory diseases; 9) Nephritis, nephrotic syndrome and nephrosis; and 10) Septicemia.

WE can prove in no limit of time that the consumption of pork causes each of these and many other diseases.

REFERENCES

1. Baulch V. Paradise Valley and Black Bottom. Detroit, MI: The Detroit News, 2004.
2. Semmes CE. The Challenges of Post-Slavery Rural and Urban Life. Racism, Health and Post-Industrialism: A Theory of African-American Health. Westport, CT: Praeger, 1996;53.
3. Stampp KM. Peculiar Institution: Slavery in the Ante-Bellum South; Vintage; 1989
4. Robinson ME, Hunter PH. Nutritional Assessment of a Predominately African-American Inner-City Clinic Population. Wisconsin Medical Journal 2002.
5. Davis CG, Lin B-H. Factors Affecting U.S. Pork Consumption. Electronic Outlook Report from the Economic Research Service. Bethesda, MD: USDA: Economic Research Service, 2005;1-18.
6. Office of Minority Health OotD, CDC. Health Disparities Experienced by Black or African Americans — United States. MMWR Surveill Summ 2005;54(1):1-3.

2

SWINE AND DIVINE LAW

Confronting Divine Mandates

Key Terms: Bible, Christian, dietary laws, disease, divine law, genetically-manufactured, Holy Quran, Muslim, parasites, pathogens, poison, trichinosis

· ·
                                                              ·
                                                              ·
                                                              ·
                                                              ·

Of all the meat products marketed today, pork has been the most controversial. It is the only meat that has been the subject of both health and religious debates. Health arguments centers on whether or not the pork is safe to eat. Religious disputes concern whether or not the divine law against eating swine meat is still *in effect*.

The major Scriptures, Holy Quran and Bible, teach against eating swine flesh, but baseless religious interpretations of these clear divine mandates have made pork a featured meat among the Christian community, and across much of the world.

Just the same, self-righteousness among some so-called Arab Muslims have blinded them to the extent that they now touch and sell swine flesh to persons they consider to be non-Muslim — as though earning profit from the sale of this despicable beast is justifiable, if non-Muslims are the ones eating it. As they see it, these so-called non-Muslims include the Black man and woman of America, particularly those who live in the inner cities. Some Arabs, like others who have come into Black communities, exploit us, opting to pour salt on our open wounds in the same satanic spirit as our enslavers, the Caucasian rulers.

If asked whether Prophet Muhammad or Jesus would do the same, these persons reluctantly admit that such divine men, who came to save humanity, would not willfully do evil and exploit those whom they were raised by Almighty God to serve. However, in a world where billions of people relegate their worship to vain talk and rituals, they feel free to practice such ungodly behaviors, while claiming to represent the Creator.

GOD'S WAY DEBATED

Indeed, the laws of God have been debated in political and socioeconomic arenas. These debates do not center on delving into the reasoning behind God's issuance of these laws. To the contrary, so-called justifications are put forth continuously to violate such laws. Everything that God said, "thou shalt not do", those who run the governments and religious institutions of this world, with respect to these laws, say, "thou shalt do". They also add *"...because in this day and time...," or "...in these modern times..."* as if to suggest that because times have changed, we can splurge in evildoing.

Some persons go as far as claiming that Jesus permitted them to eat swine as long as they prayed over it. Such is not found in the Scriptures of the Holy Quran or Bible. Ironically, such false reasoning is constantly used to justify the eating of pork. These people actually lie against Almighty God and Jesus for the sake of a pork meal. Yet, they claim that salvation rest in the Father and Son. This hypocritical behavior, in the name of divine, is absolutely unacceptable.

The dietary laws given to Moses was and is *part and parcel* of a body of laws, some of which include laws against murder, fornication, adultery, and stealing. Therefore, to suggest that this particular law is obsolete is to suggest that all the laws that accompanied it are obsolete. That is to say, if eating swine is now lawful, then so is murder. If eating swine is lawful, so is stealing. If eating swine is lawful, then so is worshipping things other than Almighty God.

In the Bible, Jesus states that He came to fulfill and not destroy the Law of Moses, or the laws given to Moses. Almighty God had a reason

---

for forbidding us to eat and touch swine flesh; and unless we can truly say that our physical bodies are made differently than those who lived 4,000 years ago, then what was forbidden to them in the interest of their health must be forbidden to us in the interest of our health. Almighty God did not remake us after He first made humans. We are made the same – flesh, bone, and blood – as those who lived 4,000 years ago.

Equally as significant is what is written in Isaiah 66:17. It states:

> They that sanctify themselves, and purify themselves in the gardens behind one tree in the midst, eating swine's flesh, and the abomination, and the mouse, shall be consumed together, saith the LORD.

Many theologians agree that the Book of Isaiah contains major prophecies about the Coming of the Messiah, and what He will do when He comes. This being the case, it is very clear that the Lord is upholding the dietary laws given through Moses. Those who eat swine flesh are threatened with a severe chastisement, in addition to the self-inflicted suffering they experience by eating this unhealthy meat.

OUTRIGHT REBELLION, INTELLECTUALLY DONE

This gross ignorance and rebellion, combined with the lack of interest in our health, on a broad scale, have many people suffering from deadly diseases such as diabetes, cancer, arthritis and heart disease. If a person can eat the injurious swine flesh, then he or she can eat just about anything. And, people eat just about anything. Additionally, if a person can break divine law by eating swine flesh, then they can easily break other divine laws. And, divine laws are broken at *will* and *whim*.

The people's violation of the law prohibiting eating and touching swine is sponsored and supported by governments. So-called government agencies condone and promote the eating of this diseased meat, often suggesting that some of the identifiable worms that harm the eater can be removed through proper food preparation.

For example, the United States Department of Agriculture's (USDA) publication about Trichinosis states:[1]

> For over a century, the knowledge that eating raw or insufficiently cooked pork could cause trichinosis has placed a stigma on pork...Even before the discovery of trichinosis, this stigma evidently existed in an undefined form. In Biblical times, pigs were referred to as "unclean" animals. The fundamental dietary laws of the Jews and the Moslems, which prohibit the eating of pork, may well have originated as a method of preventing this disease.

This publication, ridden with deception, audacity and evil, substantiates the obvious fact that the government is directly opposed to Almighty God, making it part of Satan's world, although it professes to be a government established on Christian principles.

Furthermore, what are *Biblical times*? Is the Bible only a history book, with no relevance to today's so-called modern society? Did Almighty God only exist during Biblical times? If we are living in the fulfillment of the prophecies delineated in the Bible, then are these not Biblical times, too?

Who put the stigma on pork, man or God? Is it a stigma or a divine law warning the people of imminent danger to the health of those who eat it?

Overall, the USDA's statement suggests that in these modern times, proper cooking can prevent trichinosis; therefore, there is no need to abstain from eating this meat.

In supporting this wickedness, the Centers for Disease Control and Prevention (CDC) recommends, through the document, *How to Prevent Trichinellosis*, that people wanting to eat swine need only:

> ...cook meat products until the juices run clear or to an internal temperature of 170°F and freeze pork less than 6 inches thick for 20 days at 5°F to kill any worms.

This government agency should be about preventing disease — as its name charges. Abstinence is the best method of prevention. We should consider the effort being made to eat something infested with worms. Why should anyone want to do all of that before eating this meat?

In the same document, people are warned that *curing (salting), drying, smoking, or microwaving meat does not consistently kill infective worms*. This is the same as telling a person to eat swine at your own risk; and this is precisely what anyone who eats swine is doing.

Why does Almighty God forbid us to eat swine? This is a good question, if one dares to question God. And, why should we not question God? We can and should question Almighty God; however, we are required to do so, while being in obedience to HIM. By doing this, we are assured of HIS favor, as we gain a deeper understanding into HIS mandates. Needless to say, not only do many people not question God while in compliance, they fail to do so while in rebellion to HIS laws.

Without going into details, we can emphatically state that the divine law against eating swine shows that the purpose of this animal was not and is not for human food. Understandably, no creature on earth is without purpose. The Creator of the Heavens and the Earth knows the use and purpose of every creature. Therefore, knowing HIS purpose for each creature enables us to see the value in HIS mandates regarding our involvement with those creatures, especially creatures that humans take as food.

SWINE'S INTENDED PURPOSE

The Honorable Elijah Muhammad states in the book, *How To Eat To Live (Book 2)*:

> The pig is a mass of worms. Each mouthful you eat is not a nutritious food but a mass of worms that the naked eye cannot detect. Worms thrive in the hog.

Such a statement deserves our utmost attention as it provides the reason why humans should not eat this animal. From the outset, our investigation should involve validating this statement. Is the pig a mass of worms? Is each mouthful of pork – whether ham, bacon, pork chops, pig feet, pork fried rice, ribs, chitterlings, spam, or any part of the pig taken as food – a mass of worms and not the bodacious and nutritious food people believe they are enjoying?

Fortunately, an enormity of research has already been accumulated regarding the poisonous nature of this animal. Eating this poisonous flesh has caused enough human injury and death to make the worms harbored in this flesh the most studied of all pathogens.

Almighty God, in the Person of Master Fard Muhammad, revealed the reason for making the swine — something that most people do not know. Out of Almighty God's mercy, through HIS continuous efforts to save man from self-destruction and divine chastisement, HE has given us more knowledge about this divinely-forbidden beast; perchance we may stop eating this meat.

According to what HE revealed to the Honorable Elijah Muhammad, swine was never intended for use as food. We are taught that this animal was made for medical purposes.

The Caucasian people, while confined to Europe for two thousand years, suffered numerous diseases. These diseases were the result of ignorant practices, as they lived in caves and were steeped in savagery and bestial living. This subhuman subsistence featured the most unsanitary environment known to the human family.

The history of the Caucasian people is well documented. Studies of the Paleolithic centuries come close to describing this period. The Honorable Elijah Muhammad taught that their weak physical nature made Caucasian people susceptible to many diseases. This, combined with their gross ignorance about proper hygiene and overall civility, created a harshly diseased environment. Consequently, they were exposed to multitudes of pathogens, and easily contracted chronic and infectious diseases.

The Honorable Elijah Muhammad writes:

> At that time, the Arab medical scientists did not have anything that would kill most, or probably all, of his diseases, so they made a medicine for him — that is the hog.

In making this beast, wise scientists genetically-manufactured it from the life germs of several animals, namely the cat, rat, and dog. This gave it the physiological and anatomical capabilities, as well as the nature, to serve as a repository for poison. This poison is in the form of parasites, viruses, fungi, bacteria and other poisonous microorganisms yet to be defined. The animal was biologically constructed to attract these poisons, just as a powerful magnet attracts metal.

The swine's ability to attract and harbor potent live poisons makes its flesh capable of being used as medicine. In one particular use, swine flesh, which is similar to a pus-like sponge, absorbs poison from boils in the skin. Salves are also made from this flesh. There are other medical and non-medical uses for this poisonous animal; however, the point is that swine was genetically-manufactured as a remedy for the poisons that wrecked havoc on the Caucasian people.

LOVE OF MONEY IN COMMERCE

Certainly, an animal that is a repository of poison is an animal that people should not eat. The Creator, naturally, does not want humans to eat or touch this diseased flesh. HIS love for us is demonstrated in HIS laws, which protect us from the harm this meat can and does cause when we eat it.

In rebellion against Almighty God, swine has served as an animal for commerce and labor. Profiteering has made this meat a worldwide industry. Swine is raised by the millions, and pork products are eaten all over the world. In the past several decades, the swine industry has experienced a dramatic expansion. Millions, if not billions, of people eat pork.

According to the latest statistics, swine farms in the United States (U.S.) raise over 60 million pigs each year, and the average American eats nearly 51 pounds of pork annually.[2] This divinely-forbidden meat is the seventh-largest farm commodity in the U.S., in terms of cash receipts. Approximately, 21 billion pounds of swine meat is sold annually.[3] In 2002, U.S. gross receipts of swine meat totaled 9.6 billion dollars.[4] These facts epitomize the Scriptural verse that the *love of money is at the root of evil*.

As an animal of labor, swine is used as live garbage disposals. This garbage includes anything from dead animals and bugs to despicable, filthy waste materials — collectively called *swill*. This shows that this animal has an affinity for filth.

Farmers have been able to get rid of garbage and cattle dung by feeding it to swine, while later selling the meat of this beast to humans. By doing this, they enjoy noteworthy savings and profits. *This world* gets exceptional mileage from this animal, to the detriment of those who eat it.

TOWARD DEBILITATION

Gross ignorance about how to live healthy lives has made the epidemic of chronic disease and early mortality acceptable. Few people think about the possibility of living hundreds of years. Consequently, people love to tout those who live a mere 60 or 70 years as having lived long. In addition, many love to discuss their health ailments in a celebratory manner, even boasting about their afflictions. This does not make sense.

Consistent with what is written in the Scriptures of the Holy Quran and Bible, the Honorable Elijah Muhammad declared that humans have the potential to live 200, 300, 400 — nearly 1,000 years, as did Methuselah, Noah and others mentioned in the Book of Genesis.

Many who claim to believe in the Scriptures disbelieve in this. They also disbelieve in the divine dietary laws, which are meant to give us longer life spans, making their painful and untimely demise understandable. Ignorance and rejection of God's laws can only lead to anguish and premature death.

The swine eater experiences consistent and gradual mental and physical degeneration, because the pathogens it harbors infests the eater's body. The Honorable Elijah Muhammad described this poison as *deceitful*, because its pathology is of an evil sort. This is the chief characteristic of parasites — they subversively suck the life out of those they infect.

Those who lack a meticulous and sensitive mindset regarding their health make it easy for pathogens to infest their bodies, as they can tolerate gradual death. They do everything in their power to avoid instant death, but settle for an enduringly painful demise from chronic conditions. For example, ingesting highly toxic chemicals, such as cyanide, causes acute or immediate biological reactions that lead to instant death. This type of poison is avoided because sudden death is undesirable.

On the other hand, such persons gladly ingest the poisonous worms that make up swine flesh. This poison integrates with the eater's biological systems and slowly dismantles them. The swine eater physically degenerates. The medical profession may have specific names for this deterioration, such as arthritis, diabetes, and heart disease, but in the most simplistic view, complete cellular destruction is taking place. This shows that we have a false view about life, and the potential to live far longer than what we currently regard as a long life.

REVISITING DIVINE LAW

The availability of greater scientific tools and knowledge allows us to investigate and validate the correctness of the divine dietary laws given by Almighty God. The use of scientific research, combined with the mega preaching of the Scriptures of the Bible and Holy Quran, should enable people to gain a better understanding about why God said what HE said, and does what HE does. No longer should the laws of God be absent in the mouths of those who preach religion. Just the same, no longer should religion operate in a vacuum — outside of the sciences of life upon which our heaven or hell truly rest.

Unfortunately, science is not factored into today's religious expression. Hardly any guidance from the broad religious community is offered about how people should live day-by-day and detail-for-detail. Today, many prominent preachers of religion campaign the so-called "prosperity" vision. They oppose the traditional preaching that glorified being meek and poor. Now, the motto is to "gain fortune and empowerment in the Lord." Such preaching is akin to motivational lectures.

There is some good in this approach; however, what is significantly lacking is *the means by which* this prosperity is achieved. How does a person prosper in life through belief in God? Is it relegated to shouting the name *Jesus*? Is it confined to following bits of economic strategies? Is it limited to memorizing "prosperity" Scriptural passages?

There is no prosperity in rebellion to Almighty God. Too little is mentioned about the ways and behaviors that clearly prove that those who claim belief in God are, in fact, living lives in direct rebellion against HIM. Divine dietary laws are broken on an hourly basis, participation in gambling is at an all time high, and greed and selfishness are entrenched in the minds and hearts of many who self-righteously proclaim themselves to be "of God".

When we violate the divine laws of God, consequences follow. These consequences are on autopilot. Therefore, the ailments, diseases, and anguish we confront on a daily basis are the results of the lives we live, and not the words we speak.

The consequences associated with eating pork are invasions by the worst sorts of pathogens and severe afflictions that ultimately lead to premature death. There is no prosperity in this, despite the material wealth we gain in the name of God.

REFERENCE

1. Veterinary Services AaPHIS. Facts About Trichinosis. Bethesda, MD: USDA, 1972.

2. Board AS. Hogs and Pigs: Final Estimates 1998-2002. Statistical Bulletin Number 986 NASS, USDA, 2004.

3. Davis CG, Lin B-H. Factors Affecting U.S. Pork Consumption. Electronic Outlook Report from the Economic Research Service. Bethesda, MD: USDA: Economic Research Service, 2005;1-18.

4. Otto D, Lawrence J. The United States Pork Industry 2003: Patterns and Economic Importance. 2003.

3

WHY CALL IT POISON-ANIMAL

Wisdom's Life-Saving Language

Key Terms: ambiguous, Arabic, Bible, English, germs, hazir, Hebrew, Holy Quran, khanzier, language, Medical Profession, nature, nomenclature, parasites, pig, poison, swine, ungulates.

. . . .
.
.
.
.

The use of simple, yet extraordinarily comprehensible terminology is exceptionally valuable in the conveyance of knowledge. Such is the Way of Divine. We expect Almighty God to be the Greatest Communicator, using clear and straightforward words to educate us. HIS messengers and prophets, as plain warners, are charged with the clear delivery of HIS message; therefore, they also are the greatest of communicators.

THEIR words go straight to the *nature* or root of the subject matter or issue at hand. The true reality of a thing or issue is its nature. And, because a thing's nature cannot be altered, dealing with its nature is the same as dealing with the truth. Therefore, to hide the truth, a person must hide the reality or avoid exposing the root or nature of the thing or issue in question.

Ambiguous words or terms breed ignorance. They also make people victims of deceit. We can safely say that terms or words that do not express the *nature* of a thing is meant to deceive. Such has been the case with the subject matter of this book.

Several terms are used to name or identify this animal, in addition to poison-animal. These include *swine, pig, hog, pork* and *the other white meat*. Very few people are familiar with the term *poison-*

animal, yet this is the most precise term to use when identifying this animal.

The terms swine, pig, hog, pork and *the other white meat* do not give the nature of this animal. The first three terms are aligned with this world's science of zoology, which has its own nomenclature. *Pork* refers to the meat of this animal, just as beef is the meat commodity from cattle. The latter phrase, *the other white meat*, is simply a marketing ploy to influence people to purchase and eat this diseased meat.

In many respects, the English language is contrary to the purpose of language. The divine purpose for language is to express truth and reality, on every level. This requires speaking "straight" words, which Almighty God mandates that we do so that we avoid any confusion in what we are trying to communicate.

English is considered a bastard language because it is a compilation of words from many different languages. It is corroded with terms that make it an easy language to be used as an avenue to deceive people. Many words have similar meanings and more words are added each year. Lawyers have *field days* with this language, using it to muddle the truth, which complicate matters of jurisprudence. Consequently, many guilty people go free and the innocent are incarcerated.

This is a big subject. The inadequacy of the English language is proven in the terms that refer to poison-animal, compared to the Arabic or Hebrew terms used to describe this animal. Let us briefly take up this issue.

AMBIGUOUS -VS- COMPREHENSIBLE

Several English dictionaries have similar definitions of swine. Essentially the word is defined:

> Swine identifies any of various omnivorous, even-toed ungulates of the family Suidae, including pigs, hogs, and boars, having a stout body with thick skin, a short neck, and a movable snout.

This definition does not convey the animal's nature, nor does it instruct us about how we should relate to this animal. Such a definition gives rise to indifference, because there is no indication of what this animal means in our lives. This is especially important because this beast is a part of the American society. Not knowing this vital information opens a way for humans to take this animal as a pet or as food. Such has been the case, as pigs are used as both pets and food for humans.

In the book, *The English Pig*, the authors confirm this disposition of indifference held by the general population when it comes to poison-animal:[1]

> The pig was simply a means to an end. Its purpose was to manufacture pork (or bacon). It had no personality or distinctive character.

This is exactly the way people view swine. Unfortunately, this ignorant disposition is applied to all animals. It seems that the broad sentiment when it comes to animals is: *when in doubt about the nature of an animal, eat it*. This is the default action. Humans eat all classes of animals — from single-cell microorganisms to whales.

Our lack of understanding about the nature of all creatures, including the human being, has made us victims of disease and early death, all of which is self-inflicted. This lack of understanding is rooted, in part, to language that is absent the meaning of the things we should and must know. This brings us to the terms used in other languages that describe swine.

Khanzier and *hazir* are the Arabic and Hebrew words, respectively, that describe swine.

Khanzier generally means:

> I see foul!

While hazir means:

> I see an animal regarded as the most unclean and the most abhorred of all animals.

These terms give us the nature of this animal, and how we must relate to it. How should we relate to something foul and unclean? Let us carefully consider these two words.

POISON-ANIMAL

Swine packed in a confinement house on an industrial swine facility.

The term *foul* is defined:

> Offensive to the senses; revolting; having an offensive odor, smelly; rotten or putrid.

Similar definitions include:

> Full of dirt or mud; dirty; full of impurities; polluted: morally detestable; wicked; very disagreeable or displeasing; horrid; bad or unfavorable; violating accepted standards or rules; dishonorable.

Unclean is defined:

> Foul or dirty; morally defiled; unchaste; ceremonially impure.

The word *unclean* is used in the law that forbids us to eat and touch swine. *Leviticus 11:7*, in the Bible, states:

> And the pig, though it has a split hoof completely divided, does not chew the cud; it is unclean for you.

In *Deuteronomy 14:8*, it states:

> The pig is also unclean; although it has a split hoof, it does not chew the cud. You are not to eat their meat or touch their carcasses.

Foul and unclean are adjectives that modify the noun *animal*. We can say that any animal is an *unclean animal* or a *foul animal*. Using these phrases can be misconstrued as being conditional, meaning that sometimes the animal is unclean and other times it is not; sometimes the animal is foul and other times it is not.

This disposition is also evident in how people view swine. For example, some people believe that in its raw state, pork is not good to eat, but in its cooked state, it is permissible to eat — believing that cooking this meat purifies it. This is very far from the truth, because this view is not aligned with the nature of this animal.

The Honorable Elijah Muhammad states in *How To Eat To Live*:

> But, the actual flesh of the hog is 999% poison (nearly 1000%), as taught to me by God, in the Person of Master Fard Muhammad, to Whom praises are due forever.

This means that poison is not only in the flesh, but that the flesh, itself, is the poison. Therefore, at best, a person is eating cooked poison as opposed to raw poison; cooked parasites as opposed to raw parasites; cooked fungi as opposed to raw fungi; and cooked viruses as opposed to raw viruses. Moreover, in spite of cooking, these pathogens remain active; and at all times, the flesh remains poisonous. Again, this is why swine is forbidden to eat and touch.

Let us return to "I see foul" or *khanzier*. This term, although clearly describing the nature of swine, has not stopped billions of people from touching and eating it. Sadly, it has not stopped some of those who claim belief in God – those who profess to be Christians, Muslims, and Jews – from touching or eating it. Entire nations have made swine a major commodity.

There are some people who do not eat swine, but participate in marketing and selling it. This makes them worst than those who eat it, because in claiming religious belief, they fail to demonstrate the same love that Almighty God has for humanity. Would Almighty God sell this forbidden flesh? The answer is no. How, then, can they be justified in selling it? They cannot; therefore, they stand condemned as hypocrites.

Overall, this reality shows that knowing the nature of something does not necessarily mean that we will do "right" by this knowledge. If humans were thinking and acting as humans are required to think and act, – in accordance with the law of God – knowing that something is khanzier would be sufficient to keep us away from it.

As victims of the evil dealings of those who rule and control nearly every facet of human living, we function on levels far below the level where God intends for us to function. As HIS best creation, we are required to function at the highest level. We are, however, influenced to disregard the Highest Intelligence, opting to satisfy demented urges, while in direct opposition to all that is good and righteous.

POISON ANIMAL: A NOUN

In *Problem 9* of *The Problem Book*, in *The Supreme Wisdom*, the following effects from eating poison animal are described.

> ...It is known to the Medical Profession and other wise Muslim Sons that poison animal sounds the mental power; one-sixtieth of an ounce per every ten ounces of poison animal

> ...It is also known to the civilized world that ten ounces of poison animal destroys three one-hundredths percent of the beauty appearance of a person.

Almighty God, Master Fard Muhammad, in revealing to the Honorable Elijah Muhammad, the truth about the devastating health ailments people suffer from eating this divinely-forbidden animal, used the best term available to bring us face-to-face with the reality of "foul". This term is *poison animal*.

Why poison animal? Let us start by defining poison:

> A substance that causes injury, illness, or death, especially by chemical means; something destructive or fatal; a substance that inhibits another substance or a reaction: a catalyst poison.

When this definition is applied to swine, it becomes clear that this is an animal that causes injury, illness, and death. Synonyms for *poison*:

Adulteration, bacteria, bane, blight, cancer, contagion, contamination, corruption, germ, infection, malignancy, miasma, toxicant, toxin, toxoid, venin, venom, virus

This sheds light on what to expect from eating poison. These terms are associated with disease and death, and represent the vast scope of what should be considered poison or the result of poison.

Now, by placing the term *poison* in the context of the Arabic and Hebrew terms khanzier and hazir, our understanding of the nature of swine is fortified a zillion-fold. We can now say, "I see a *foul animal* that is *the most unclean and the most abhorred of all animals* because it *causes injury, illness, or death;* therefore, I will not touch or eat it."

POISON ANIMAL

A diseased and dead hog in a confinement facility. Will the meat from this animal still make it to the grocery store?

Therefore, *poison* is not used to modify the word *animal*; it is used as part of the noun, itself — *Poison Animal* — that identifies and gives the nature of this animal. This term is hyphenated (poison-animal) throughout this book for simplicity.

What person would intentionally eat an animal that is foul, abhorred, and poisonous? How might people respond if asked whether they ate poison-animal, as opposed to asking them if they ate swine? What person would confidently say, "Yes, I eat poison-animal, I am a *poison-animal eater*?" Few people would do so.

REFERENCES

1. Malcolmson R, Mastoris S. The English Pig. London: The Hambledon Press, 1998.

4

Poisons in Poison-Animal

Dangerous Swine Pathogens

Key Terms: acute, asymptomatic, bacteria, cecum, cestode, Cryptosporidium, cysticericosis, edema, enterocytes, eosinophilia, epidemiology, farrowing, flora, fungi, hyperplasia, ileum, immune system, immunological, infection, lesions, lymphatic, metabolize, microbiological, mycoplasma, nematode, obligate, parasitologists, parasitology, parasites, pathogens, pathology, proliferative enteropathy, quintessential, repository, scouring, septicemia, systemic, trematode, Trichinella, trichinoses, ulceration, viral, viruses

This subject can be divided into two areas — the pathogens this world's scientists have identified in poison-animal and what Almighty God has revealed concerning the poisonous nature of poison-animal. Although what this world's scientists know about poison-animal is enough to make any self-loving person refrain from eating it, millions of people still eat it. A reason for this could be that this scientific information is not widely available. For the most part, this research is confined to those who are involved in the fields of agriculture, animal sciences and parasitology.

Nevertheless, because eating poison-animal is divinely prohibited, discussions surrounding this animal should take place in our religious services. We can reasonably assume that few discussions and sermons about God's dietary laws occur. It appears that many people eat pork so easily and openly – with no feeling of guilt or shame – that they must be unaware that this meat is divinely-forbidden. Therefore, there is a high probability that few people know about the divine mandate against eating poison-animal.

This also means that many people are ignorant about certain aspects of what they claim to believe. We must become students, and not just listeners, of what we claim to follow.

In Book 2 of *How To Eat To Live*, the Honorable Elijah Muhammad compares the poisonous natures of poison-animal and rattlesnakes, which sets the premise for our understanding of the magnitude of poison in poison-animal. He writes:

> The hog, according to the teachings of God, in the Person of Master Fard Muhammad, to Whom praises are due forever, is very poisonous. It contains more poison than a rattlesnake…It is not the flesh of the rattlesnake which is so poisonous, but the sac full of poison, which it carries in its mouth. When the rattlesnake strikes it empties the sac of poison into your flesh. This causes death to the victim, if he does not receive attention quickly. But, the actual flesh of the hog is 999% poison (nearly 1000%) as taught to me by God, in the Person of Master Fard Muhammad, to Whom praises are due forever. This poison is not going to kill you instantly. It drags you along for many years.

This animal's remarkable ability to store poison is exemplified in this account. Most of us would run from a rattlesnake because our demise is inevitable when we come across this dangerous snake. Many animals also run from this snake. Contrarily, the poison-animal does not run. It sees a meal slithering its way. We have learned from the Honorable Elijah Muhammad that poison-animal can take the bite of a rattlesnake, stomp the rattlesnake into the ground, and then eat it. What other animal can do such? Again, this animal was made a repository for poison, including poison from lethal snakes.

Two key points from the words of the Honorable Elijah Muhammad must be noted. The first exposes the ignorant mindset among the human population that if something does not kill you quickly, it is okay to deal with — even to take as food. With this mindset, bearing chronic pain from long-term suffering is more acceptable than instant death.

We must beg the questions: When the quality of our lives are extremely disrupted to an extent that we spend most of our time dealing with chronic diseases, is this not nearly equivalent to being dead? Is life merely about being able to breathe, or is it about being productive with our lives?

The old folks use to say, "all suffering ain't death", as a way of warning loved ones about doing harmful things that may not kill them suddenly, but may lead to sickness down the road. Our elders, knowing the difficulties of suffering under enduring diseases, have learned that illness and death are not close in time or space. People can suffer many years, even decades, before dying.

The second point is that Almighty God revealed the extent of the poisonous nature of poison-animal — that the actual flesh is 999 percent poison because the swine contains 999 germs. We know the animal is unclean; however, just what "unclean" meant, we did not know. We are now learning the vast scope of this. It is becoming clearer why God forbids us to eat and touch poison-animal.

HUMANS AND PATHOGENS

Some researchers estimate that about one-quarter of the world's population is infested with one or more of the major helminthes.[1] The term *helminth* originates from the Greek language, and means worms. Helminthes are higher, multi-cellular parasites with specialized organs. By actions, helminthes are considered animals, and are of two major types: flatworms or *Platyhelminthes* (flukes and tapeworms); and roundworms or *Nematoda*.

To date, parasitologists have identified approximately 300 species of helminthes and over 70 species of protozoa that infect humans.[2] In the research paper, *History of Human Parasitology*, the following is stated:

Many of these are rare and accidental parasites, but we still harbor about 90 relatively common species, of which a small proportion cause some of the most important diseases in the world, inevitably, these are the ones that have received the most attention.

A parasite or helminth lives completely at the expense of other creatures. These other creatures can be plants or mammals, which are known as "hosts" after infection occurs. In the majority of cases, parasites infect animals and humans.

In the paper, *Foodborne and Waterborne Parasites,* a similar assessment is given:

> More than 72 species of protozoan and helminth parasites can reach humans by food and water, and most of these infections are zoonoses.

Zoonoses are parasites that flourish in animals and are highly transmittable to humans. The primary mode of human transmission is through eating the flesh of the infected animal. Many parasites can only live in mammals, making them the burden bearers of parasitic infections. Anyone who eats meat must keep this fact in mind.

Of the 72 pathogens, 11 helminthic species thrive in the flesh of different animal species, and subsequently, infect humans when this flesh is eaten; 20 trematode species, four cestode species and seven nematode species infect humans through the consumption of seafood; and six species of Cryptosporidium contaminate food and water. Diagnostic and detection methods are available for only a few parasites, and these testing mechanisms are not full proof — neither do the makers of these machines claim them to be error-free.

The *Encyclopedic Reference of Parasitology* lists several challenges parasites must solve to thrive in mammals:[3]

- They must develop successful strategies for finding hosts.
- They must find methods of attachment and/or partial or total penetration into their prospective hosts.
- They must become able to feed on their host's tissues or fluids, and must be able to metabolize the nutrients obtained.
- They must develop mechanisms to protect themselves from attacks by the host's defenses (immune system).
- They must establish a high reproduction rate in places that allow their offspring to be transmitted to other hosts.

The latter two challenges point to an important pathological aspect of parasitic infections. Through circumventing the immune system, infections are usually asymptomatic. This means that there are usually no acute or alarming symptoms associated with the parasitic infection. Occasionally, acute symptoms do occur,[4] and when they do, the person is diagnosed with the parasitic disease. For example, the Trichinella parasite is the most familiar worm in poison-animal, and causes acute symptoms, leading to a diagnosis of trichinosis.

Unfortunately, unless acute symptoms occur, people are not diagnosed with the infection although they are infected. The result is, unbeknown to them, that the parasites will continue to infest and thrive in their bodies, usually for the rest of their lives.

Parasites seek out places in the body from which their offspring can transfer to new hosts, such as reproductive organs or places near them. The female breast and uterus are preferred sites for parasites, as well as other pathogens.

Parasites also populate the most muscular places in the body, such as the diaphragm, liver, legs and arms. People who eat meat prefer these areas because they are the meatiest. Therefore, in both cases, parasites are assured a high probability of host-to-host transmission.

HIJACKING OF THE IMMUNE SYSTEM

Many helminthes extensively migrate through body tissues, causing tissue damage and triggering adverse immunological reactions, most of which do not lead to acute symptoms.[5] The most obvious forms of direct damage from parasitic infections are blockages of internal organs, and the inordinate pressure exerted by growing parasites and cysts on these organs.

The least obvious yet most death-dealing damage is systemic, involving the immune system. The host's immune responses, although useful for diagnosing parasitic infections, usually are not protective. Therefore, activation of the person's immune system does not necessarily mean the body is being defended. In most circumstances, the immune system is being turned against the person by the parasites' ability to arrest and control it.[6]

The damage comes from immune-mediated inflammatory changes in the skin, lungs, liver, intestine, central nervous system, and eyes — as parasites migrate to and settle in these organs. In addition, systemic changes such as eosinophilia, edema, and joint pain reflect allergic responses that occur throughout the body.

Some arthritic conditions are nothing more than allergic reactions to parasitic infections. Some people may find this difficult to believe because the pain seems continuous, unlike what we experience in environmentally induced allergies from pollutants. In comparison, these two types of allergies are distinct as apples to oranges. For example, the pollutant, such as pollen, eventually leaves the air, or the allergy can be alleviated through medications; however, parasites remain intact in the muscles and joints. Therefore, the allergic responses they induce remain constant.

Helminthes release large amounts of antigens and enzymes to divert the host's immune responses or even exhaust the immune system, rendering it ineffective in protecting the person from the current threat, as well as from opportunistic infections from other pathogens. These workings characterize the words of the Honorable Elijah Muhammad — *... this poison is not going to kill you instantly. It drags you along for many years.*

Among the reasons for the latter is the duration of parasitic infections. These creatures have an uncanny ability to remain in the host, while rendering permanent and irreversible changes to muscles and other body tissues.

The intestine is the area most infected by parasites. The global incidence of intestinal infections is estimated at nearly two billion people.[7] These infections tend to be chronic, with high re-infection rates, because people tend to continue with the dietary habits that made them vulnerable to the initial infection.[8]

Many dietary habits that lead to infections are rooted in traditions.[9] Certainly, the consumption of poison-animal is a tradition of Black America, having its origin in the chattel slavery era.

KNOWN PIG PARASITES

It should come as no surprise that an animal that feeds on filth is a repository for many harmful pathogens — parasites, viruses, bacteria, and fungi. This is an understatement. The poison-animal is actually overwhelmed with poison. The Honorable Elijah Muhammad writes in *How To Eat To Live*:

> He (poison-animal) is so poisonous and filthy, that nature had to prepare him a sewer line and you may find the opening on his forelegs. It is a little hole out of which oozes pus. This is the filth of his body that cannot be passed fast enough.

People who eat pig feet should be very familiar with the sticky pus that gets all over their hands and mouths. This pus is not natural gravy or seasoning, as the old folks used to call it. This is poison in its purest form. The makers of this creature put the sewer line there because it is close to the ground. For example, in cities, sewer lines are almost always underground or near the ground because drainage is easier.

The scientists who manufactured poison-animal probably did not expect that people would eat it, not to think of eating the feet of this animal. Poison-animal may very well be the only animal whose feet are eaten. People do not even eat chicken or cow feet.

HELMINTHES GALORE

Poison-animal is severely plagued with microorganisms, in a manner like no other animal. Approximately 20 species of parasites infect poison-animal, and of these, five to 10 are most common, often coexisting in a single animal.[10] So, the Trichinella parasite, although the most popular, is not the only parasite people must confront when eating poison-animal.

The most virulent parasites make their way from the stomach to the intestinal tract, which serves as a place of long-term residence or a place from which parasites launch their anatomy-wide attack. Many parasites that infest poison-animal remain in the small intestine and colon, while just as many invade other organs.

Parasitic infestation causes an array of health consequences, often impeding the poison-animal's growth and development into that fat and meaty commodity from which comes bacon, ham, ribs and spam.[11] Many of these diseases feature poor digestion, gut ulcerations, blood loss, widespread arthritic conditions, and neurological damage.

Parasites also invade the lungs, where they interfere with respiration, causing pneumonia and other respiratory conditions. In all cases, parasites make the poison-animal susceptible to continuous ambushes by other pathogens, resulting in a litany of other ailments and diseases. Death often results from severe infections from many different pathogens simultaneously plaguing the poison-animal.

The Honorable Elijah Muhammad called our attention to the fact that this animal does not have a long lifespan. The poison-animal, although having its snout constantly in the feeding trough, is an animal under an extraordinary amount of suffering, pain, and agony. Yet, it continues to eat anything and everything, caring nothing about the consequences incurred by the filth it gobbles down. This makes the poison-animal the dumbest and silliest of all animals, even more stupid than the donkey.

Here, we must reiterate that the poison-animal is a robust, even quintessential, helminth carrier. Undeniably, those who eat poison-animal ingest the same parasites, fungi, viruses, and bacteria that wreck havoc on the animal. The adverse workings of these parasites also make poison-animal eaters susceptible to opportunistic infections from other pathogens.

This being the case, poison-animal eaters experience the same astonishingly painful health consequences that the animal suffered until its death. They suffer with these ailments until their deaths. Respiratory, neurological and muscular disorders of the most awful kind plague poison-animal eaters.

Unfortunately, those experiencing these ailments often continue to eat this poison meat, while descending into debilitating conditions. This mindset is similar to that of the poison-animal, which cannot stop eating filth regardless of the suffering it incurs by eating it.

ECONOMICALLY IMPORTANT PARASITES

The research paper, *Parasitic Helminthes of the Pig: Factors Influencing Transmission and Infection Levels*,[10] highlights the parasites that are the most economically important to the industrial swine industry. These particular parasites prematurely kill many animals before their time of slaughter; thereby, creating an unwanted and unplanned expense to poison-animal farmers.

Major Poison-Animal Parasites

Helminth Species	Life Cycle	Characteristics
Ascaris summ	Direct	Thick-shelled, highly resistant, long-lived eggs, strong acquired resistance.
Oesophagostomum spp.	Direct	Low, non-protective acquired resistance infection accumulate with age.
Trichuris suis	Direct	Thick-shelled, highly resistant, long-lived eggs strong acquired resistance infection in pigs.
Strongyloides ransomi	Direct	Free-living generation of adults - percutaneous penetration - transcolostral transmission and strong immunity infection of piglets.
Hyostrongylus rubidus	Direct	Moderate acquired resistance infection of adult pigs.
Metastrongylus spp.	Indirect	Earthworm immediate host - strong acquired resistance infection in pigs.
Stephanurus dentatus	Direct	Earthworm transport host - long prepatent period.
Ascarops strongylina	Indirect	Coprophagous beetle intermediate host - infection of outdoor pigs.
Physocephalus sexalatus	Indirect	Coprophagous beetle intermediate host - infection of outdoor pigs.
Macracanthorhynchus hirudinaceus	Indirect	Coprophagous beetle intermediate host - infection of outdoor pigs.
Trichinella spp.	Indirect	Larvae in flesh - transmission by predation and (crypto-)cannibalism - wide host spectrum (zoonose).
Taenia solium	Indirect	Metacestodes in pigs-man infected by eating raw flesh (zoonose)
Schistosoma japonicum	Indirect	Freshwater snail intermediate host - infection by cercariae - wide host spectrum (zoonose).
Dicrocoelium dendrriticum	Indirect	Slugs and ants intermediate host - infection by eating ants - wide host spectrum (zoonose).
Fasciola hepatica	Indirect	Freshwater snail intermediate host - infection by metacercariae - wide host spectrum (zoonose)

From the research paper: Parasitic Helminthes of the Pig: Factors Influencing Transmission and Infection Levels

These parasites are listed in the table above, along with key characteristics associated with their transmission processes. Only 15 pathogens are listed, which is a far cry from the 999 pathogens that poison-animal harbors. These parasites, however, are very formidable in dismantling the health of the poison-animal eater, just as they do the poison-animal.

The following sections briefly describe several of the most abundant of these parasites. Various species of these parasites also infect humans.

ASCARIS SUUM (ROUNDWORM)

These parasites are stout and pinkish, often having curved tails; and are among the largest, measuring more than eight inches in length when adults. These are the most common parasites in industrial swine operations, infecting approximately 70 to 80 percent of the herd.

The adult worms live in the small intestine, grazing the gut lining and ingesting particulate and liquid materials. The parasites compete for nutrients in the intestine, causing the animal to experience vomiting and other intestinal ailments.

A single female parasite produces up to a million eggs a day. These eggs are resistant to cold and disinfectants, and are sticky and easily transported by cockroaches, beetles, flies, birds and workers' boots and clothing. When another pig swallows the eggs, they hatch in the stomach or small intestine. The larvae that emerges penetrates the gut wall and is carried to the liver through the bloodstream.

The larvae settle in the liver for a short period, then are swept through the bloodstream to the lungs. From there, the larvae are coughed up, settling in the surrounding environment. Consequently, the poison-animal eats the larvae, which return the parasites to the small intestine. There, they stay, growing and maturing to produce offspring, and the cycle begins again.

Health damage to the poison-animal occurs as the larvae migrate through the liver and lungs. During the liver migration, white scar lesions form, commonly known as *milk spots*. The lung migration makes the poison-animal susceptible to respiratory problems, such as mycoplasma and viral pneumonias.

In addition to liver damage, a few other illnesses include inflammation of the liver caused by allergic reactions to the parasites' migration; colic or gut pain caused by the parasites' grazing, forcefully nipping and stretching of the gut walls as they grow. Constipation develops, often causing obstruction of the gut.

TRICHURIS SUIS (WHIP WORM)

These parasites are slender, approximately two inches long, and are found in the cecum and upper colon of the poison-animal. The cecum is a large pouch at the beginning of the large intestine. This parasite has been isolated from approximately 30 to 40 percent of poison-animal farms in the United States (U.S.).

The parasites burrow into the cecum and intestinal wall, disrupting nutrient absorption and causing secondary bacterial and viral infections in the animal. Female worms sporadically produce many eggs.

The eggs are passed in the feces and become infective in several weeks. These eggs are also very resilient and can last in the environment up to ten years. The poison-animal ingests the infective eggs, which then hatches the larvae. The larvae migrate to the cecum where they become adults. There, they produce eggs and the process starts over.

The parasites' penetration of the gut lining causes irritation, blood loss, and other bowel disorders and diseases.

OESOPHAGOSTOMUM (NODULAR WORM)

This parasite is about an inch long when it reaches adult size, and as with several others, lives in the animal's colon. The name "nodular worm" derives from the nodules produced by the larval stage of infection. These nodules are formed as a fibrotic or immune response in the walls of the cecum and colon to "wall off" the larvae.

Larvae that escape nodule formation emerge in the gut and mature into adults. The female parasites lay eggs, which are passed in the feces and hatch in areas in poison-animal facilities, such as farrowing pens and dirt lots. The eggs persist in the environment for many years.

The poison-animal becomes infected with the larvae when eating from their troughs. The worms migrate to the gut where they stay. The infected poison-animal experiences diarrhea, decreased appetite and poor weight gain. Intestinal scouring, resulting from infection, often occurs.

STRONGYLOIDES (THREADWORM)

This is a tiny intestinal parasite. Female worms live in the wall of the small intestine, where they lay eggs. The eggs are passed in the feces of poison-animal, contaminating areas such as farrowing pens, dirt lots and pastures. Larvae are ingested through water and feed, and may also penetrate the animal's skin. Larvae also pass in colostrums (milk); thereby, infecting the newborn poison-animal at the first nursing.

Prenatal infections are also known to frequently occur. In fact, this parasite is known to cause congenital infections in both animals and humans. Severe infections cause intensive intestinal scouring, which results in acute dehydration.

STEPHANURUS DENTATUS (KIDNEYWORM)

This stout, black and white parasite is approximately one inch long and is found in the poison-animal's kidney and in the tissue areas around the kidney. Because this infection occurs in and around the kidneys, the eggs are passed in the urine and hatch in farrowing pens and other areas of the farms where poison-animal dwell. The poison-animal becomes re-infected by ingesting the larvae, having their skins penetrated by the larvae, or by eating infected earthworms. The larvae, after entering the poison-animal, migrate from the small intestine to the liver.

From the liver, larvae migrate to areas around and in the kidneys and even lodge in back muscles. Most of the damage caused by this parasite is found in the liver and in muscle tissue surrounding the liver. Other infected organs include the lungs and spleen.

Outbreaks of Stephanurus infection have occurred in southern Missouri with both breeding stock and market-weight poison-animal.

METASTRONGYLUS APRI (LUNGWORMS)

These parasites are between one and two inches long, slender and white. They live in clusters deep in the respiratory tract (bronchioles). The eggs are coughed up, swallowed and passed in the feces; and are ingested by earthworms. The earthworms are ingested by poison-animal while feeding.

From the small intestine, the larvae circulate through the lymphatic system, travel through the heart and then reach the lungs. The "thumping" or "coughing" sound often heard among poison-animal herd is a sign of infection. Pneumonia is the most common illness caused by this infection.

ANTIBIOTICS: NASTY SAGA CONTINUES

As if the knowledge of these dangerous poison-animal parasites were not enough to *drive home* the poisonous nature of this divinely prohibited flesh, the pathogens targeted for antibiotics continue this eye-opening saga. This further strengthens Almighty God's case in forbidding us to have any dealings with poison-animal. Again, HE forbids those practices and behaviors that injure us. HE is not trying to take our so-called "good-eating" away from us. HE best knows the foods that are good from those that are death-dealing.

The term *antibiotic* is defined:

> A substance, such as penicillin or streptomycin, produced by or derived from certain fungi, bacteria, and other organisms, that can destroy or inhibit the growth of other microorganisms. It means "against life" or "destructive to life".

Antibiotics are widely used in the prevention and treatment of infectious diseases. These agents, which are microbiological, are used to destroy bacteria, molds and fungi that endanger the lives of humans and animals. Unlike vaccinations, antibiotics are used during the course of infection.

Virulent bacteria and fungi have caused widespread death among the human population throughout the annals of history. Pathogens that have antibiotics developed to fight them are serious threats to health and life.

More than a dozen potent antibiotics, namely antibacterial and antifungal compounds and groups of compounds, have been used in industrial poison-animal operations. No other animal has received this level of attention. The effort of poison-animal farmers to ward off dangerous pathogens from an animal that is made to attract these poisons is futile, yet they go all out to do so — spending millions of dollars developing potions, salves and remedies.

The antibiotics injected in poison-animal include various salts of bacitracin, chlortetracycline, dynafac, mycostatin, oxytetracycline, oleandomycin, penicillin, streptomycin, bambermycins, tilmicosin, and tylosin. Many people are unfamiliar with these terms. Notwithstanding, the use of such a wide array of chemicals confirms the poisonous nature of this beast.

We must note that fierce debate surrounds the abundant use of antibiotics in livestock and how this practice is causing antibiotic resistance among humans who eat this flesh, rendering them susceptible to harmful pathogens.[12] Many believe that it is becoming increasingly difficult to ward off pathogens as many are developing antibiotic-resistance, which makes them more virulent.

The majority of the antibiotics used in poison-animal operations are targeted for the following pathogens: *Escherichia coli*, *Salmonella*, *Lawsonia intracellularis*, *Pasturella*, *Mycoplasma*, and *Leptospirosis*. Poison-animal eaters must know exactly what that pork chop, pig foot, chitterling, bacon strip, and sausage patty brings into their lives. Eating this divinely-forbidden meat brings into the life of the poison-animal eater the most feared pathogens known to the animal kingdom, mankind, and man; as well as contamination from a barrage of chemical and microbial agents injected into this animal. The price of eating this divinely-forbidden, diseased meat is too high.

Escherichia coli, Salmonella, and Lawsonia intracellularis are the most economically important bacterium, as they infect poison-animal by the millions and, consequently, millions of people. The following sections briefly describe each of these pathogens.

ESCHERICHIA COLI

There are hundreds of strains of the bacterium Escherichia coli (E. coli); however, *E. coli O157:H7* is an emerging cause of foodborne illness. This pathogen was first recognized during an outbreak of severe bloody diarrhea in 1982. Investigators traced the outbreak to contaminated hamburgers, and since then, most infections have allegedly been associated with eating ground beef.

However, the epidemiology of E. coli O157:H7 has become an important research topic as this pathogen has been detected in manure from different animals, including poison-animal.[13] It has been found in the vicinity of industrial poison-animal operations. For example, the presence of E. coli O157:H7 in poison-animal feces has been reported in Japan, Norway, Chile, and the U.S. Health authorities know that this strain persists in the poison-animal's intestinal tract.

The Centers for Disease Prevention and Control (CDC) estimates that each year 73,000 cases of E. coli infection and 61 deaths occur in the U.S. Bloody diarrhea is the most common symptom of these infections.

Additionally, this infection causes hemolytic uremic syndrome (HUS), a serious condition marked by the destruction of red blood cells and renal failure. Nearly 10 percent of those with E. coli infections experience this serious complication. Overall, HUS is the principal cause of acute kidney failure in the U.S., and most cases are caused by E. coli O157:H7.

The use of antibiotics to treat E. coli infections are controversial because of the risk factors associated with these medicines — often causing more serious disease outcomes. This is due, in part, to the elimination of competing and natural bacteria in the intestine, which causes an imbalance to the organ.

SALMONELLA

More than 2,400 serotypes of Salmonella exist, and numerous types cause a variety of ailments in poison-animal. A few of these include *Salmonella typhimurium* and *Salmonella choleraesuis*. Both also cause disease in humans. Salmonella infections in poison-animal herds are known to spread quickly following exposure. The pathogens multiply rapidly in the intestine before spreading to other internal organs.

Salmonella pathogens are among the most common causes of foodborne diseases in humans, and poison-animal meat (pork) has been implicated as the primary source of these outbreaks. The disease caused by Salmonella infection is called Salmonellosis.

Salmonellosis is the most frequently reported foodborne illness in the U.S., and is the second most common foodborne illness worldwide. The CDC estimates that 1.4 million cases occur each year in the U.S., which results in approximately 600 fatalities.

Clinical symptoms of human Salmonellosis include fever, abdominal pain, diarrhea, nausea and vomiting. Dehydration can become severe and life threatening. The disease may also result in septicemia and death.

LAWSONIA INTRACELLULARIS

Lawsonia intracellularis is an obligate intracellular bacterium that causes a condition known as *proliferative enteropathy*. This condition is frequently diagnosed in poison-animal raised in the U.S., and throughout the world.[14] A National Animal Health Monitoring Service survey estimated that about one-third of the herds in the U.S. are affected with this parasite, costing the poison-animal industry tens of millions of dollars.

This infection causes proliferative lesions in the small and large intestines, hyperplasia of crypt enterocytes and a decrease in goblet cells. Generally, this means that the intestinal tract is severely altered and mangled by this pathogen.

The infection is marked by an acute form of bloody diarrhea due to massive hemorrhage of the intestinal tract. Death usually results in severe infections.

Lawsonia intracellularis infections have been linked to ulcerative colitis in humans.[15] Ulcerative colitis is a disease that causes inflammation and sores, known as ulcers, in the intestinal lining. The inflammation usually occurs in the rectum and lower part of the colon, but sometimes affect the entire colon.

The inflammation causes diarrhea and ulcers in places where the inflammation has killed the cells in the intestinal lining. These ulcers often bleed, producing pus. This condition is a known cause of colon cancer.

CHEMOTHERAPEUTICS AND ANTHELMINTHICS

In addition to antibiotic agents, many chemotherapeutic and anthelminthics (dewormers) compounds are added to the diet of or injected in poison-animal to help control parasites. Parasitic infestation is prevalent in poison-animal facilities.

We noted that parasites reduce growth rate and feed efficiency, damage animals' organs, and predisposes them to infection by other pathogens. Parasitic infections add $1 to $14 to the feed and maintenance cost of each animal. Additional losses pile up when the animals die or infected tissues are condemned at the slaughter plant.

Anthelminthics are man-made chemical compounds. A few of these include carbadox and sulfas. Some of the common agents include dichlorvos, pyrantel tartrate, Hygromycin B, ivermectin, levamisole, fenbendazole, Thiabendazole and Piperazine. Again, these names are foreign to most people; nevertheless, poison-animal eaters must contend with these potent chemical compounds when eating this diseased meat.

No one has assessed the impact on humans from ingesting anthelminthes. We can assume that some level of impact is occurring, to the detriment of those who eat this poisonous meat.

999 GERMS, NEARLY 1000% POISONOUS

· ·

The parasites and bacteria discussed in this chapter are only a drop in the bucket of a multitude of poisons that comprise the biological makeup of the poison-animal. Again, the poison-animal contains 999 germs, which makes this animal nearly 1000 percent poisonous. This world's knowledge of this animal is not remotely close to what Almighty God knows.

This fact is substantiated in *The Problem Book* of *The Supreme Wisdom*, wherein Almighty God, in the Person of Master Fard Muhammad, revealed the level of knowledge used to build *this world*, which is ruled by Caucasians.

In *Problem 25* of the *Problem Book*, we are taught that the Public Library of Cairo contains three million, seven hundred thousand books, of which sixty-thousand are exclusive to Mathematics, Astronomy, Language and other Sciences of Life. Moses, after being commissioned by Almighty God to civilize the Caucasian people living in the caves of Europe, took one of each book from these categories with him to carry out this assignment. This world is built from this knowledge, which represents the lowest level of available knowledge in the areas of math, astronomy, language and other life sciences.

From a ratio standpoint, this world's know-how in these areas is a mere one-sixtieth-thousandth of what the Original Man has available in the Public Library of Cairo, not to mention the other vaults of books and sacred text unknown to this world.

Therefore, this world has an exceedingly inferior knowledge about poison animal compared to what the Original Man knows about this poison-animal. This is why the Honorable Elijah Muhammad warns us about following a society where the mandates of God are habitually violated.

This self-destructing world is evidence of its rulers' gross rebellion and severely limited knowledgebase. Such a stupendous level of rebellion obliterates the little knowledge given to this inferior world. Savagery is now the order of the day, and the consumption of poison-animal pathogens makes people participants in the destruction of their world.

REFERENCES

1. Chan MS. The global burden of intestinal nematode infections-fifty years on. Parasitol. Today 1997;13:438-443.
2. Cox FEG. History of Human Parasitology. Clin. Microbiol. Rev. 2002;15(4):595-612.
3. Mehlhorn H. Encyclopedic Reference of Parasitology. 2 ed. New York: Springer, 2001.
4. Despommier DD, Karapelou JW. Parasite life cycles. New York, N.Y: Springer-Verlag, 1988.
5. Andreassen J. Interactions between intestinal tapeworms and their hosts: present knowledge and problems. Parassitologia 1997;39:259-267.
6. Borkow G, Bentwich Z. Chronic Immune Activation Associated with Chronic Helminthic and Human Immunodeficiency Virus Infections: Role of Hyporesponsiveness and Anergy. Clin. Microbiol. Rev. 2004;17(4):1012-1030.
7. Maizels RM, Yazdanbakhsh M. IMMUNE REGULATION BY HELMINTH PARASITES: CELLULAR AND MOLECULAR MECHANISMS. Nat Rev Immunol 2003;3(9):733-744.
8. Else KJ, Finkelman FD. Intestinal nematode parasites\cytokines and effector mechanisms. Int J Parasitol 1998;28:1145-1158.
9. Macpherson C. Human behaviour and the epidemiology of parasitic zoonoses. Int J Parasitol 2005;35(11-12):1319-31.
10. Nansen P, Roepstorff A. Parasitic helminths of the pig: factors influencing transmission and infection levels. Int J Parasitol 1999;29:877-891.
11. Tubbs RC, Corwin RM. Common Internal Parasites of Swine. Vol. 2005 University of Missouri Extension, 1993.
12. von Baum H, Marre R. Antimicrobial resistance of Escherichia coli and therapeutic implications. Int J Med Microbiol 2005;295(6-7):503-511.
13. Feder I, Wallace FM, Gray JT, Fratamico P, Fedorka-Cray PJ, Pearce RA, Call JE, Perrine R, Luchansky JB. Isolation of Escherichia coli O157:H7 from Intact Colon Fecal Samples of Swine. Emerging Infectious Diseases 2003;9(3):380-383.
14. Smith DGE, Mitchell SC, Nash T, Rhind S. Gamma Interferon Influences Intestinal Epithelial Hyperplasia Caused by Lawsonia intracellularis Infection in Mice. Infect. Immun. 2000;68(12):6737-6743.
15. Pitcher M, M. Goddard, McOrist S, Cummings JH. Ulcerative colitis and porcine proliferative enteropathya common bacterial etiology. Gastroenterology 1995;108(Auppl 4):A894.

5

TRICHINELLA INFESTATION

Super Poison-Animal Parasite

Key Terms: anaerobic, angiogenesis, antigens, asymptomatic, calcification, copulate, encapsulate, enteric, foodborne, genomic, hypoxia, lumen, malaise microbes, morphological, nurse-cell, obligate intracellular, parasite, pathogen, pathogenic, poison-animal, reemergence, sylvatic, T. spiralis, Trichinella, trichinosis (trichinellosis), zoonotic

I n the article, *How Does Trichinella spiralis Make Itself at Home?*, it states:[1]

Unlike the majority of intracellular parasites, Trichinella occupies the host cell without killing it, and thus it is considered one of the most successful of all parasitic symbionts, because it is this strategy that enables it to travel world-wide and extend its range into all parts of the earth in which the scavenging of carrion occurs.

The Trichinella (trichina) spiralis parasite is among the oldest parasites known to man, principally because it has a long history of causing human disease. Even today, this pathogen is a major problem in the international commerce of poison-animal meat.[2]

For nearly 170 years, health researchers have studied Trichinella.[2] Hundreds of research articles, dating back to the mid-1800s, have been written about this parasite. Generally, Trichinella is an *obligate intracellular parasite* in both its larval and adult forms; therefore, it causes a series of biological and molecular changes in animals infected by it.[3] The clinical manifestation of this infection is called trichinosis or trichinellosis.

EMERGING & REEMERGING

Researchers postulate that the poison-animal becomes infected with the Trichinella parasite by eating the flesh of its kind, particularly those that die in the poison-animal industrial facilities; eating infected rats; and eating garbage containing infected poison-animal meat scraps.[4] Because of this, preventive measures include keeping rats away from industrial poison-animal facilities and making sure that dead poison-animal carcasses are immediately removed from the poison-animal population — two tasks that are impossible to achieve for a number of reasons.

TRICHINELLA FEMALE PARASITE

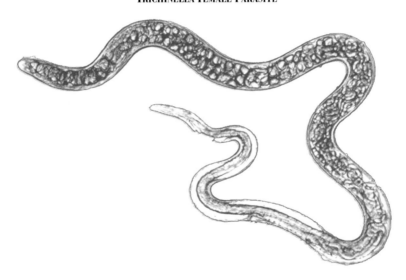

The female Trichinella continues to produce offspring as long as she stays in the person's small intestine

One reason is that industrial poison-animal operations dominant the agriculture industry. The harsh conditions in confinement houses, where poison-animal are crammed, foster disease and death. Keeping rats away from these filthy facilities is impossible. In addition, the rat is in the very nature of the animal; therefore, the same pathogens the rat attracts are attracted to the poison-animal.

More realistically, any so-called measures used to eliminate Trichinella infection in poison-animal are futile. Why is this? The poison-animal is precisely that — poisonous. The process through which this animal was genetically-manufactured made poison an intrinsic part of the animal's nature.

Again, Trichinella has few rivals among mammalian parasites for both host range and geographic distribution because all stages in the parasite's life cycle (larval and adult) occur in the same host. This is unlike many other parasites whose development occurs through stages involving different hosts.

TRICHINELLA SPECIES

In this close-up of the Trichinella parasite, we can see that its anatomy enables it to
burrow into intestine and muscle tissue.

For example, in filarial zoonotic infections, two mammals and a mosquito are usually involved in the complete transmission cycle. Humans are infected when stung by a mosquito that has stung an infected animal. The mosquito carries the infected-stage larvae from the animal to the human.

For many years, parasitologists assumed that T. spiralis was the only species of Trichinella. To date, however, both *encapsulated* and *non-encapsulated* species exist.[5] Encapsulation is the process through which parasites develop cysts in muscle tissues. The larvae live in these cysts.

The encapsulated species include *T. spiralis, T. nativa, T. britovi,*[6] *T. murrelli*, and *T. nelsoni*. The non-encapsulated species are *T. pseudospiralis, T. papuae* and *Trichinella zimbabwensis*.

Human infections have been reported for each species.[7] Researchers continue to uncover and discover differences in pathologies among species. For example, experiments revealed that cyst formation differs between T. spiralis and T. pseudospiralis.[6]

Generally, there are biological and pathological variations among Trichinella species and genotypes.[8] These factors have significant bearing on why this parasite is very formidable. In fact, this is part of the reason why trichinosis is a re-emerging infection.

In the research paper, *New Aspects of Human Trichinellosis: The Impact of New Trichinella Species*, the following is noted:

> Trichinellosis is a re-emerging zoonosis and more clinical awareness is needed. In particular, the description of new Trichinella species such as T. papuae and T. murrelli and the occurrence of human cases caused by T. pseudospiralis, until very recently thought to occur only in animals, requires changes in our handling of clinical trichinellosis, because existing knowledge is based mostly on cases due to classical T. spiralis infection.

Trichinosis outbreaks caused by various species of Trichinella occur in countries regardless of socio-economic development. Some people would like to believe that so-called industrial nations have livestock populations that are parasitic free, but this is not the case. Both industrialized and developing countries, alike, are burdened with increasing levels of pathogenic infestations.

Data points to the fact that Trichinella infection continues to have a global impact, affecting countries on every continent. For example, infections are prevalent throughout the Asian region, as major outbreaks have been reported in China, Thailand and other neighboring countries.[9]

A caption of this threat in Asia is presented in the paper, *Areas of Uncertainty in the Management of Human Trichinellosis: A Clinical Perspective*:

> In China, for example, there have been more than 500 reported outbreaks of human trichinellosis since 1964, with an estimated 25,161 cases and 240 deaths. An estimated 200 to 600 cases are reported annually in just one Thai province with a population of approximately 1 million people...

Trichinella infection has been a public health problem in Mexico, and Central and South America for quite some time. Countries such as Argentina and Chile are beset with high rates of infections.[10] Trichinella infections have drastically reemerged in Europe,[11] and infections in North American countries, including the United States, have been well known since the parasite's discovery.

Notwithstanding, this newly discovered Trichinella species, *T. spiralis* holds a special place among the Trichinella genus. This parasite is now widely recognized as the only species with high infectivity for swine, rats and mice.[12]

T. spiralis is also infective to sylvatic hosts such as wild boars, bears, and rodents,[13] and it has been identified in North American red foxes and coyotes.[14] T. spiralis has a higher larvae production rate than other species of the genus,[15] and is the least freeze-resistant species.[16]

For these reasons, we take up the historical background, life cycle and associated pathologies related to human infection with the T. spiralis parasite.

HISTORICAL BACKGROUND

In 1835, a British medical student, observing a cadaver, discovered that parasites were the cause of the deceased's *sandy diaphragm*.[17] Lesions caused this sandiness. A lesion is an abnormal change in the structure of an organ or part of an organ, which is usually caused by an injury or disease. These parasites tattered the diaphragm, causing it to resemble hairs positioned in spiraling formations; hence, the name "Trichinella" — from Greek origin, meaning *hairy*.

The diaphragm is a broad muscle that forms the floor of the thoracic cavity and is intricately involved in breathing. The thoracic cavity is the area of the chest or thorax. It is a part of the body between the neck and the abdomen and is supported by the dorsal vertebrae, the ribs, and the sternum. It is the place where the heart and lungs are situated.

DIAPHRAGM, INFERIOR VIEW

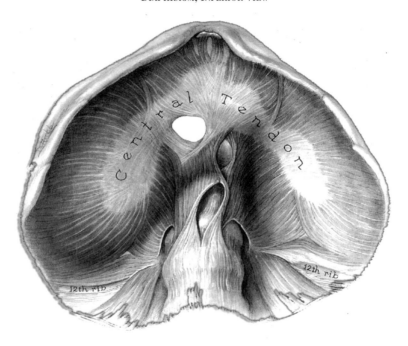

Trichinella infects major muscle areas in the body, such as the diaphragm located in the thoracic cavity.

The diaphragm is the prime mover of inspiration. There is little doubt that T. spiralis parasites, by invading the diaphragm and adversely affecting breathing, were involved in that person's demise.

A decade later, researchers implicated poison-animal as the cause of this trichinosis.[18] Subsequently, researchers occupied themselves with the study of this parasite, documenting the epidemiology and pathology associated with the various aspects of infection.

From the discovery of Trichinella in 1835, scores of research papers have been written about the workings of T. spiralis. For example, in an 1875 paper, *Trichinosis*, the symptoms of a patient suffering from this infection is described:[19]

> ...The symptoms were mainly those of gastroenteritis; muscular pains were conspicuous ...In one of the fatal cases, however, the muscular tenderness was so great that the patient could scarcely be moved...

He continued to explain that after the patient's death, examination of the muscles revealed that it was crammed with T. spiralis, to the tune of 100,000 worms per cubic inch. Although the researcher did not give details regarding the duration of the illness, we can assume that the enormous infestation of this parasite was indicative of a chronic or long-term infection.

Again, the workings of parasitic infections reveal a calculable, deliberate and systematic invasion of its host. The patient probably endured great pain and suffering, to the very end.

An 1895 article, *A Case of Trichinosis*, detailed the death, by trichinosis, of a German man:[20]

> ...The temperature was 103.5° F. The face was red, the eyes bulging in the sockets, and the conjunctivae red and swollen and raised above the level of the cornea...He grew weaker and died on April 17th.

The researchers indicated that there was no difficulty identifying the characteristics of Trichinella infection in this fatality. The common symptoms of acute infection, which resembled enteric fever, were malaise, backache, pain in the limbs, fever, typhoid-type stools, and rose-colored spots. Additionally, this case reaffirmed the hypothesis of a two-week incubation period after ingestion of infected meat, during which the parasites migrate from the intestines to the muscles.

THORACIC CONTENTS

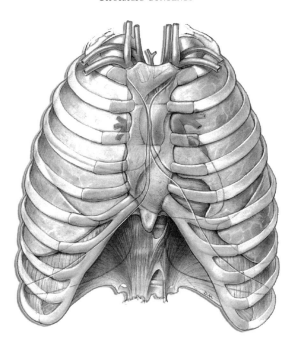

The heart, lungs and diaphragm are situated in the thoracic cavity. This muscular area is a primary target of parasites because they can build many cysts in this area.

Another research paper, *The Pathology of Trichinosis*, published in 1912, featured a dispute between two researchers about aspects of trichinosis pathology:[21]

...He finds that the female trichina penetrates into the intestinal walls, usually stopping in the subepithelial layer and not passing the muscularis mucosae. In opposition to the statement of Cerfontaine, M. Romanovitch finds that the parasite does not reach the mesenteric lymphatic glands. The female parasite deposits the larvae in the lymphatics or sometimes in their neighbourhood. The larvae reach the blood stream by way of the lymphatics.

Several interesting aspects of trichinosis were revealed in this article. Romanovitch further postulated that the larvae may reach serous cavities, such as the *pleurae* or *peritoneal* cavity, but because conditions are unfavorable, they often perish. He also noted that the most striking morphological feature of trichinosis was the widespread loss of the intestinal lining, which made the patient vulnerable to infections by other *microbes*.

Time has proved the former point untrue, as parasites migrate through this area; however, the later viewpoint makes sense. As the primary means through which nutrients enter the bloodstream, the intestinal epithelium also has protective or delimiting functions. Anything that weakens this barrier reduces its ability to stop foreign substances from entering the bloodstream. Therefore, the likelihood that other opportunistic pathogens will seize upon a weakened intestinal lining is very high. In fact, it is guaranteed.

In addition, Romanovitch was convinced that fever, enlargement of the spleen, abscesses, and fatal septicemia were due to microbes. These microbes, he posited, were inoculated by the T. spiralis as they passed through the mucous membrane.

The concept of inoculation called attention to the production of toxins by the parasite. He found in the serum of infected rats and guinea-pigs, toxic properties, which developed nine days after the ingestion of T. spiralis-infected meat.

Other studies focused on the problem of determining the most effective procedures to diagnose trichinosis, which included estimating the number of deaths caused by the disease. An estimate of trichinosis prevalence was presented in a 1937 article, *Diagnosis of Trichinosis in the Living*:[22]

> The prevalence of trichinosis in the United States, to which we recently called attention, has been emphasised by D. L. Augustine, who points out that the examination of diaphragms at necropsies in Boston has shown an incidence of 27.6 per cent.

This meant that Trichinella was involved in nearly 30 percent of the deaths in Boston during that time. As a meat-eating society, scientists thought it reasonable to make such a radical assessment; and the study of diaphragms during autopsies assured accuracy of infection. We should also keep in mind that this study occurred decades before the industrialization of poison-animal farming.

TRUNK, SUPERFICIAL DISSECTION, LATERAL VIEW

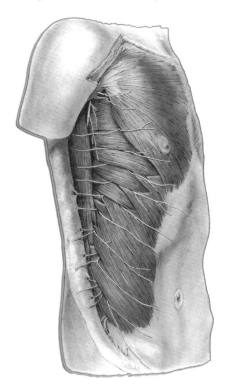

The Trichinella parasites have extraordinary high reproduction rates, infecting nearly every muscle tissue in the body. The entire back and side muscles are targets of these parasites.

After addressing the inadequacies of current procedures used to diagnose the severity of infection, the author concluded:

...diagnosis is a tedious affair and may be made only after the medical attendant has weighed a careful history and the results of a complete physical examination against those aids which the laboratory can give him.

Historically, there has been difficulty diagnosing trichinosis. This is a common problem with many parasitic infections, and hinges on several factors.

First, with the advent of numerous "named" diseases whose symptoms are similar to trichinosis, medical practitioners have a broader selection of diseases from which to choose. Trichinosis is usually not atop the list of possibilities.

In this contemporary medical environment, this disease is considered antiquated, although parasitologists warn of the reemergence of this parasitic infection. Nevertheless, the probability that Trichinella infection may be pandemic is not considered, yet billions of people eat billions of pounds of poison-animal each year.[23] This fact suggests that the chances of widespread Trichinella infection are great. If medical examiners decided to test diaphragms for Trichinella, they would discover that Trichinella infections are pandemic.

Secondly, although both acute and mild cases of trichinosis exist, only acute incidences raise flags, thus warranting urgent medical attention and proper diagnoses. However, in mild cases, effective diagnosis may or may not occur because these cases involve transient symptoms that mirror other ailments. Therefore, if perchance Trichinella parasites have made mincemeat of a patient's heart, consequently causing heart failure, medical professionals may likely render a diagnosis absent the true cause — T. spiralis infestation.

Continuing with the estimated number of people infected with T. spiralis, a 1938 article, *Trichinosis in the United States*, called attention to national infection rates:[24]

> The cases of human trichinosis reported to the Public Health Service in 1915-36 number very nearly three thousand, and since 1930 the annual quota has risen from under a hundred to over five hundred — i.e., from a case rate of about 1 per million population to 4.5 per million.

In response to this information, researchers contended whether this statistical increase denoted a real increase in infection or was it the result of the medical community's increased interest in the disease, which led to an increase in incidence reporting. Of course, it could have been either or both.

With this being the case, increased incident reporting is common in the epidemiology of potentially endemic, epidemic or pandemic diseases. Interest always builds in combating diseases that are considered growing threats to public health. Governments usually require more effective reporting in order to make a proper assessment of the disease's scope and severity. This allows for the targeting of resources and preventive measures at the most vulnerable populations.

Researchers also noted that trichinosis cases were becoming milder. They hypothesized that the increase in mild cases resulted from changes in the preparation of poison-animal products. Formerly, such products were usually prepared from one poison-animal. A single infected animal would produce severe cases in a limited population.

However, the advent of centralized and commercial food manufacturing involved more than one animal to produce meat products. For example, ground meat is usually made from two or more animals — with one animal being more infected than the other animals. Poison-animal is infected by parasites in varying degrees.

The hypothesis is that meat from an infected poison-animal would be mixed with the meat from a less infected poison-animal, producing a "diluted" form of Trichinella infection; thereby, making infections milder.

To one extent, there is no "real" diluted form of a T. spiralis parasite. When the T. spiralis worm is ingested, it goes to work to make a home for itself. On the other hand, the number of worms ingested may determine the severity of infection. Eating a piece of poison-animal that contains millions of parasites would likely produce a more severe reaction than eating a piece that contains thousands of worms. This, although logical, is not always the case.

The severity of the reaction to the infection is predicated on the poison-animal eater's immune system. Eating more parasites can potentially, compromise the immune system in a way that eating fewer parasites would not. However, the sensitivity of the person's immune system can respond in the same manner whether millions or thousands of worms infest the body. These variables shed light on the difficulty involved in diagnosing T. spiralis infection, specifically how it presents as mild and asymptomatic incidences.

After postulating that 27 million people were infected with T. spiralis, the author of a 1963 article, *Trichinosis*, explained the difficulty associated with identifying and assessing this infection:[25]

> ...Few of us have much experience of trichinosis, not because it is rare but because most infestations in man are inapparent or unrecognised. That a "typical case"can be both dangerous and puzzling is shown by an account from Nova Scotia.

In this account, 11 people in two families were infected. Each person had the four cardinal features of the disease — fever, orbital edema, myalgia, and eosinophilia. Lethargy was also prevalent. The source of infection was meat from a homebred poison-animal.

The researcher noted that of all the specific tests to diagnose the disease, the most effective was a biopsy of the deltoid muscle. This muscle is located in the arm/shoulder area. It was also noted that, in some cases, the number of cysts were not related to the severity of the illness.

This sheds additional light on the previous hypothesis that the level of infection does not correlate to the severity of symptoms. Although some people may experience acute symptoms, all people suffer degenerative conditions from this parasitic infection, particularly if the infection persists, unbeknown to the infected person.

In this study, concern was also expressed about the effectiveness of several common methods used to test for trichinosis. These methods included the Suessenguth-Kline flocculation test; the complement-fixation test; and the latex agglutination test. The results were inconclusive for all methods. In addition, other methods — serial electrocardiograms, serum-protein analyses, and estimation of the glutamic oxaloacetic transaminase — also failed.

Also noted, was the absence of an eosinophil reaction in the fatal case of trichinosis. Eosinophils are a type of white blood cell associated with infections by parasites or other pathogens. Previously, researchers held that an *eosinophil reaction* was a sure bet in recognizing Trichinella infections. This case proved this untrue; nonetheless, eosinophilia is still a hallmark of infection.

AXILLA/CLAVPECTORAL FASCIA, ANTERIOR WALL

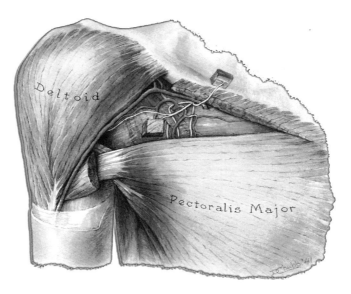

Biopsy of the deltoid area is the most frequently used method of testing for Trichinella infection. Parasites populate this area because of its muscle content.

LIFE CYCLE

▪ ▪

The life cycle of the T. spiralis parasite is well documented. As with many other helminthes, infection requires that a host (in this case, a human) ingest the flesh of another host (in this case, poison-animal) containing the encysted, viable Trichinella larvae.[26]

Again, Trichinella is also found in bears, foxes, dogs and other mammals. People eating the meat of these animals are at risk of infection. Humans, however, usually eat more poison-animal than they do bears, foxes, and dogs, although bear meat has become popular. Dog meat is eaten heavily in Asian countries, such as China, but still does not compare to the consumption of poison-animal.

In the United States, poison-animal is the primary meat through which Trichinella infection occurs. Eating poison-animal, in the form of pork chops, pig feet, ham, hog-mogs, and pork-fried rice, to name a few popular dishes, causes T. spiralis infestation.

When the T. spiralis cysts are ingested, the hot gastric juices in the stomach frees the larvae from the cysts. The liberated infectious larvae invade the small intestines, where they mature to adults over the next 18 to 24 hours. While there, the adult worms mate. This mating is a substantial activity and causes damage to the intestinal lining, which produces long-term, even lifetime injuries.

In the research paper, *Trichinellosis: human disease, diagnosis and treatment*, the damage done to the small intestine is described:[27]

> In most patients with trichinellosis, pathomorphology of the intestinal mucosa includes lesions to the epithelium involving the brush border, lamina propria and smooth muscles of the jejunum, deformation of villi, stimulated enterocyte proliferation at villi margins, hyperplasia in the crypts of Lieberkühn and the presence of massive cellular infiltrates (of mononuclear and plasma cells) in the mucosal sublayer...

This description provides more details concerning the damage that was noted in the 1912 article, where it was pointed out that opportunistic microbes infest the poison-animal eater because of a severely damaged intestinal lining.

These parasites continue to copulate throughout the various stages of infection. The constant eating of poison-animal leads to continuous reinfection, which makes intestinal damage persistent.

The pregnant female parasites increase in size and burrow deep into the intestinal wall, lodging between the duodenum and the large intestine. While there, the parasites release larvae into the mucosa and lymphatic system. This occurs around the fifth day of infection and continues for weeks. Again, with continuous reinfection, this activity is constant.

Between the fifth and 16th weeks, each female releases thousands of eggs; and this high rate of reproduction continues as long as the parasites remain in the intestine.

SMALL AND LARGE INTESTINE, IN SITU

Trichinella parasites burrow deep into the intestine causing permanent damage to the intestinal lining. This makes the person vulnerable to scores of other pathogens that infest and infect the body.

The larvae travel the bloodstream and lymphatic system as free-swimming organisms in the lumen of blood vessels and lymph vessels, respectively. From these circulatory highways, they migrate through and invade muscle tissue in various organs.

The parasites migrate to the striated muscle areas, where they take up residence by lodging deep into the muscle tissue. Their residence is constructed through the alteration of the muscle cells; thereby forming a unique type of cell.

Scientists have termed this unique cell the *nurse-cell*. This nurse-cell is an enlarged muscle cell, melded into a thick collagen capsule.[28]

This cell, literally, serves as the home of the Trichinella larvae for decades to come, even beyond the person's death.

The nurse-cell formation is also known as an encasement process. The muscles are calcified during the formation. Calcification is a process that makes the muscles *stony* and *inflexible*. Collagen and other substances produce the calcified muscle.

Revisiting the "sandy" diaphragm of the 1835 cadaver, which led to the identification and naming of this parasite, we can better understand that the calcification of the diaphragm made the person incapable of breathing. This caused severe respiratory conditions. Given the current pandemic of respiratory problems, health authorities should investigate parasitic infections as a leading cause of these ailments. Again, biopsies of diaphragms during autopsies may reveal a pandemic of Trichinella infection.

This encasement process takes between six and 24 months to complete. The deliberate, but gradual calcification process provides insight into the workings of parasites. The worms must be intelligent as to not trigger the host's immune system when setting up their communities. A faster development cycle would alarm the immune system and put an end to the parasites' efforts.

Although the immune system responds on some level, thereby destroying some larvae; the majority of encysted larvae remain viable and infectious for many years. Of course, this is not good for the person infected with Trichinella. This hardening process of the muscle tissues causes chronic pain in both muscles and joints. People who eat poison-animal usually live with this pain until they die.

PERMANENT MUSCLE ALTERATIONS

The formation of the nurse-cell has been well studied and is a unique event in the workings of T. spiralis and other parasites that live in the host's muscles. This phenomenon has deemed the Trichinella parasite among the most, if not the most, intelligent parasite known to man. The nurse-cell is the key to this parasite's ability to infest the poison-animal eater and other mammalian hosts for decades without immediately killing the hosts. Eventually, death does come to the poison-animal eater because of the chronic complications caused by the infection. This death puts an end to long bouts with chronic pain and anguish.

NURSE-CELL IN MUSCLES

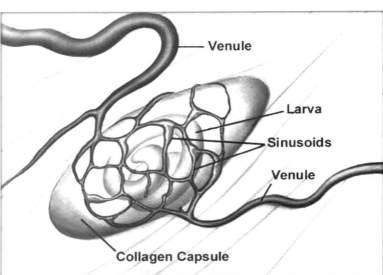

Trichinella forms a nurse-cell in the muscles, which serves as the permanent home of its larvae. The person's muscles are completely and permanently altered. The parasite uses the person's biological systems to survive and thrive.
(Courtesy of The Trichinella Page: http://www.trichinella.org/bio_nursecell.htm)

The striated muscles most infested by this worm include the diaphragm, the muscles around the eye, and the pectoral, deltoid gluteus, and bicep muscles. The Trichinella worm, as with any parasite, has the mission to thrive — that is, populate in great numbers and extend its presence throughout the human body. Therefore, it invades other organs and areas of the body, eventually making its way into the spinal fluid and up to the brain, causing late-stage infection wherein death of the poison-animal eater is certain.

For the sake of clarity, the nurse-cell phenomenon is likened to humans constructing communities in forests or other previously uninhabitable lands. These lands must be altered to properly serve our needs. Such alterations include, but are not limited to, land excavation, re-routing or constructing waterways, installing water and electrical systems, constructing roadways, and building houses and other facilities. We use the life of the earth to support our lives.

In T. spiralis' case, it uses physical and biological resources that support human life to foster life for itself. Moreover, just as we have both intentionally and unintentionally abused the environment in constructing our civilizations, the poison-animal eater experiences the same as T. spiralis works to ensure its survival.

T. spiralis uses several mechanisms to achieve long-term survival through its nurse-cell. The collagen capsule, which is built from within the cell, is at the core.[29] Collagen synthesis begins between the seventh and eighth day of infection and continues throughout the infection. Therefore, the parasites go to work immediately to secure their future.

Two types of collagen are synthesized to form and support the nurse-cell.[30] One of the two types is synthesized up to the third week of infection, while the other continues throughout infection. The latter assures T. spiralis continuous protection. Again, using human activities, this process is akin to how we remodel our homes and municipal infrastructures.

In constructing the nurse-cell, the parasite secretes enzymes within the infected cell.[31] These antigens alter the muscle cell by reprogramming the cell's genomic makeup.[32] According to scientists of all types of muscle diseases, none *resembles the complexity of permanent changes associated with those encountered during nurse-cell formation.*

Nurse-cell formation features high metabolic activities, and demonstrates a significant divergence from normal muscle cells in several fundamental aspects of metabolism. For example, studies show that the nurse cell consumes significantly greater amounts of glucose/mg of proteins than normal skeletal muscle cells.[33] The nurse-cell is dramatically altered, and devoid of muscle-specific proteins. This parasite literally makes a new type of tissue from the poison-animal eater's muscle tissue.

This phenomenon supports the Equation presented in *Problem 9* of *The Problem Book* in *The Supreme Wisdom:*

> It is also known to the civilized world that ten ounces of poison animal destroys three one-hundredths percent of the beauty appearance of a person.

ENCAPSULATED LARVA IN MUSCLES

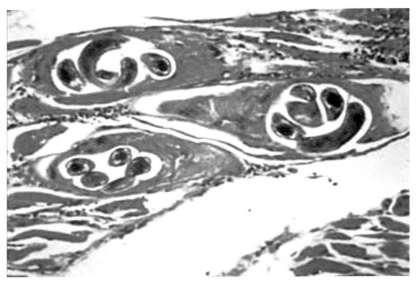

T. spiralis larva infested in muscle tissues through encapsulating and later calcifying the muscle tissues.

The dermatological destruction is a manifestation of the internal destruction of tissues and organs; and according to current knowledge regarding the formation of the nurse-cell, the damage done to the tissue is permanent.

The formation of the nurse cell has some affect on the poison-animal eater's overall metabolic processes, and may give rise to or play a part in metabolic disorders such as diabetes and thyroid conditions. Scientists have not taken up this specific issue; however, the scope of the physical, neurological, and metabolic destruction is very extensive. Researchers have only scratched the surface of T. spiralis' effect on the human vessel.

ARREST OF LIFE-SUSTAINING PROCESSES

Long-term host–parasite relationships depend on the ability of the parasite to perform metabolic activities to support its life. The most important of these are acquiring nutrients and eliminating wastes. The parasite must accomplish this through the poison-animal eater's biological systems.

In accomplishing these tasks, the Trichinella parasite attracts highly permeable sets of blood vessels to the surface of the collagen capsule.[34] This assures the provision of a continuous source of nutrients, in the form of various metabolites. The parasite is also able to rid itself of waste material through these blood vessels. In the scientific community, the way T. spiralis carries out these chores is of significant interest.

In attracting blood vessels, T. spiralis causes oxygen deficiency to occur in the surrounding tissues. This condition is called *hypoxia*. The lack of oxygen causes cellular degeneration, which manifests as wounds or lesions. These injuries invoke the process of *angiogenesis* — the process by which new blood vessels are formed as part of the healing process.

Angiogenesis leads to the upregulation of substances vital to tissue repair. One substance is *vascular endothelial growth factor* (VEGF). VEGF is a key mediator of angiogenesis. This growth factor stimulates cellular construction activities such as proliferation, sprouting, migration, and morphogenesis. These activities are similar to what occurs in natural wound healing.

Returning to the paper, *How Does Trichinella spiralis Make Itself at Home*,[1] it states:

> A constant, low level production of VEGF peptide (also known as vascular permeability factor) after circulatory rete formation is complete implies a permanently heightened state of vascular permeability, and would present obvious advantages to the parasite for maintaining itself within the host for long periods of time.

This suggests that T. spiralis' workings are perpetual. In studies, VEGF mRNA has been detected in the cytoplasm of developing nurse-cells, beginning the seventh day of infection. Findings also suggest that VEGF remains upregulated throughout the infection period. In fact, the entire series of these activities begin at the outset of nurse-cell formation and continue throughout the lives of the millions of T. spiralis parasites living in the poison-animal eater's body.

Much remains unknown about the broad health impact of these processes; however, we do know that any form of short or long-term parasitic infection threatens the person's life in various ways, making parasitic infections a leading cause of major chronic diseases, including cancer.

For example, scientists have suggested that continuous angiogenesis causes cancer; thus, inhibiting angiogenesis is becoming a principle target in cancer treatment. The research paper, *Molecular Targets of Growth, Differentiation, Tissue Integrity, and Ectopic Cell Death in Cancer Cells,* makes this point clear:[35]

> Cancer cells continue to grow, lose their differentiation, and are found beyond their tissue boundaries, where they survive...The surrounding host cells, such as fibroblasts, macrophages, leukocytes, et cetera, and the extracellular matrix play an important role in the creation of the microenvironment for the cancer cells to invade. Blood and lymph vessels are not only the transporters of nutrients and metabolites for the primary tumor, these vessels also transport cancer cells to distant sites, where they metastasize. Angiogenesis and host cells are targets in cancer treatment.

Moreover, VEGF is fundamental in the process of tumor growth and metastatic dissemination and is also a primary target.[36] Reasonably, if angiogenesis supports the parasites' cysts, then the same processes support tumors. In fact, many parasitic cysts are mistaken for tumors. The parasite's extraordinary ability to arrest the poison-animal eater's natural cell repair processes brings about carcinogenesis in other places throughout the body.

LIFE AFTER DEATH

Scientific evidence reveals anaerobic capabilities of T. spiralis during nurse-cell maintenance. This means that the parasites can live in the absence of atmospheric oxygen.[37] This ability hinges on the nurse-cell's energy metabolism, which also explains how the parasite remains infectious for days, weeks and months after the death of the poison-animal. T. spiralis remains viable even in decaying muscle tissue.

We must emphasize that the nurse-cell formation could not occur without T. spiralis' ability to arrest the intercellular communication systems of its host and use a wide range of secreted signaling molecules to carry out its own developmental and life-sustaining programs. T. spiralis secretes some 40 different antigens (proteins) to ensure that these activities are carried out.[38] Through this signaling infrastructure, it dictates many activities of the host's internal biological systems.

These activities reveal that something substantial is taking place in the poison-animal eater. Because of this, some researchers have suggested that T. spiralis may be more virus-like than worm-like.[39] Studies are increasingly showing that the mechanisms by which some parasites usurp the immune system mirrors those of viruses.[40]

For example, chronic immune activation, which is a hallmark of human immunodeficiency virus (HIV) infection, is also present in human populations with helminthic infections.[41] This being the case, people who are suspected of having a virus may, in fact, have a parasitic infection.

PREVALENCE OF TRICHINOSIS

As noted at the outset of this chapter, trichinosis is now considered both an emerging and reemerging disease.[42] There are several reasons for this. The expansion of global trading has substantially increased the risk for the transporting of meat products infected with Trichinella and other foodborne pathogens, particularly in *ready-to-eat* pork products.[43]

NOTION OF MEAT INSPECTION

For this reason, some countries have adopted so-called preventive measures to *inspect* and *qualify* poison-animal meat before importing, exporting or making this diseased meat available to the public. Industrialized countries, such as the U.S. have these mechanisms.

Just the same, many countries that export poison-animal have no meat inspection regulations in place; however, meat inspection is only a notion. The primary methods used to detect Trichinella are ineffective and allows certain amounts of pathogens to remain in the meat.[44] In other words, these methods have detection thresholds, and amounts above specific thresholds may trigger concern. However, all poison-animal meat that passes inspection contains pathogens.

Additionally, with poison-animal industrial farming rapidly increasing around the globe, outbreaks of parasitic infections are the norm.[45] The growth of the poison-animal industry has made unsanitary conditions and pathogenic infestations among poison-animal the rule rather than the exception.

We, again, reiterate that poison-animal is precisely that — poisonous, as it possesses 999 germs, making it nearly 1000 percent poisonous.

NUMBER OF PEOPLE INFECTED

Various attempts have been made to estimate the global incidence of trichinosis. Inadequate incidence reporting among all countries has made such assessments impossible. Some researchers, however, have estimated that as many as 11 million people experience trichinosis.[46]

Such an estimate is not worth the thought that went into it. Trichinosis is an acute response to Trichinella infection. The deceptive workings of parasites do not produce acute reactions in a way where the disease can be considered a major threat. On the other hand, the pandemic of chronic disease among the human population shows the prevalence of asymptomatic infections of Trichinella and other parasites.

Therefore, a more accurate estimation of Trichinella infection among the human family is to count the number of people eating poison-animal. The poisonous nature of this divinely-forbidden animal confirms that infections are assured for those who eat this meat.

PREVENTION IS A NOTION

Poison-animal profiteers, which include government agencies that certify diseased meat products, deceive people into believing that poison-animal pathogens can be destroyed by "adequately" cooking this meat. This is sheer speculation and recommendations regarding such advice have been notably inconsistent.

For example, in 1963, the USDA recommended cooking poison-animal for a few minutes at 125.6°F to sufficiently kill the Trichinella parasites.[47] Later, other groups suggested cooking this diseased meat at 140°F, which is nearly 15 degrees above the 1963 recommendation. To date, the USDA recommends cooking poison-animal at 170° F.

What about those who followed the 1963 recommendations? How about those who cooked this meat at 140°F? Can their relatives file law suits against the government for wrongful deaths or negligence? These persons were deceived in their rebellion against the divine law prohibiting the eating and touching of this beast.

The truth is that multitudes of parasites, bacteria, fungi and viruses persist in poison-animal meat no matter how the meat is prepared.

REFERENCES

1. Despommier DD. How Does Trichinella spiralis Make Itself at Home? Parasitology Today 1998;14(8):318-323.
2. Gajadhar AA, Gamble HR. Historical perspectives and current global challenges of Trichinella and trichinellosis. Veterinary Parasitology 2000;93(3-4):183-189.

3.   Capo V, Despommier D. Clinical aspects of infection with Trichinella spp. Clin. Microbiol. Rev. 1996;9(1):47-54.

4.   Campbell WC. Trichinosis revisited – Another look at modes of transmission. Parasitology Today 1988;4(3):83-86.

5.   Murrell KD, Lichtenfels RJ, Zarlenga DS, Pozio E. The systematics of the genus Trichinella with a key to species. Veterinary Parasitology 2000;93(3-4):293-307.

6.   Rodriguez-Osorio M, Gomez-Garcia V, Benito R, Gil J. Trichinella britovi human infection in Spain: antibody response to surface, excretory/secretory and somatic antigens. Parasite 2003;10(2):159-64.

7.   Bruschi F, Murrell KD. New aspects of human trichinellosis: the impact of new Trichinella species. Postgrad Med J 2002;78(915):15-22.

8.   Bolas-Fernandez F. Biological variation in Trichinella species and genotypes. J Helminthol 2003;77(2):111-8.

9.   Takahashi Y, Mingyuan L, Waikagul J. Epidemiology of trichinellosis in Asia and the Pacific Rim. Veterinary Parasitology 2000;93(3-4):227-239.

10. Ortega-Pierres MG, Arriaga C, Yepez-Mulia L. Epidemiology of trichinellosis in Mexico, Central and South America. Veterinary Parasitology 2000;93(3-4):201-225.

11. Pozio E. Trichinellosis in the European Union: Epidemiology, Ecology and Economic Impact. Parasitology Today 1998;14(1):35-38.

12. Kapel CMO, Webster P, Lind P, Pozio E, Henriksen S-A, Murrell KD, Nansen P. Trichinella spiralis, T. britovi, and T. nativa: infectivity, larval distribution in muscle, and antibody response after experimental infection of pigs. Parasitology Research 1998;84(4):264-271.

13. Dame JB, Murrell KD, Worley DE, Schad GA. Trichinella spiralis: genetic evidence for synanthropic subspecies in sylvatic hosts. Exp. Parasitol. 1987;64:195-203.

14. Appleyard GD, Conboy G, Gajadhar AA. Trichinella spiralis in sylvatic hosts from Prince Edward Island. J Wildl Dis 1996;34:158-160.

15. Pozio E, La Rosa G, Rossi P, Murrell KD. Biological characterization of Trichinella isolates from various host species and geographical regions. J. Parasitol 1992;78:647-653.

16. Pozio E, La Rosa G, Amati M. Factors influencing the resistance of Trichinella muscle larvae to freezing. In: Campbell WC, Pozio E, Bruschi F, eds. Trichinellosis. Rome: Istituto Superiore di Sanitá Press, 1994;173-178.

17. Owen R. Description of a microscopic entozoon infesting the muscles of the human body. Trans. Zool. Soc. Lond 1835;1:315-324.

18. Dupouy-Camet J. Trichinellosis: a worldwide zoonosis. Veterinary Parasitology 2000;93(3-4):191-200.

19. Trichinosis. The Lancet 1875;106(2728):843.

20. A Case of Trichinosis. The Lancet 1895;146(3773):1596.

21. The Pathology of Trichinosis. The Lancet 1912;179(4632):1557-1558.

22. Diagnosis of Trichinosis in the Living. The Lancet 1937;230(5952):750-751.

23. Grivetti LE, Corlett JE, Locket CT. Food in American History Part 5: Pork. Nutrition Today 2002;37(3):110-117.

24. Trichinosis in the United States. The Lancet 1938;231(5981):903-904.

25. Trichinosis. The Lancet 1963;281(7277):371-372.

26. Mortensen JE. Trichinosis: epidemiology and diagnosis. Clinical Microbiology Newsletter 1995;17(12):89-92.

27. Kociecka W. Trichinellosis: human disease, diagnosis and treatment. Veterinary Parasitology 2000;93(3-4):365-383.

28. Despommier DD. Trichinella spiralis and the concept of niche. J. Parasitol. 1993;79:472-482.

29. Ritterson AL. Nature of the cyst of Trichinella spiralis. J. Parasitol 1966;52:157-161.

30. Polvere RI, al. e. Trichinella spiralis: synthesis of type IV and type VI collagen during Nurse cell formation. Exp. Parasitol. 1997;86(191-199).

31. Despommier DD, al. e. Trichinella spiralis: secreted antigens of the L1 larva localize to the cytoplasm and nucleoplasm of infected host cells. Exp. Parasitol. 1990;71:27-38.

32. Criado-Fornelio A, de Armas-Serra C, Gimenez-Pardo C, Casado-Escribano N, Jimenez-Gonzalez A, Rodriguez-Caabeiro F. Proteolytic enzymes from Trichinella spiralis larvae. Veterinary Parasitology 1992;45(1-2):133-140.

33. Montgomery J, Augostini P, Stewart G. Glucose uptake and metabolism in the Trichinella spiralis nurse cell. Int J Parasitol 2003;33(4):401-12.

34. Baruch AM, Despommier DD. Blood vessels in Trichinella spiralis infections: a study using vascular casts. J. Parasitol 1991;77:99-103.

35. Derycke L, Van Marck V, Depypere H, Bracke M. Molecular targets of growth, differentiation, tissue integrity, and ectopic cell death in cancer cells. Cancer Biother Radiopharm 2005;20(6):579-88.

36. Ribeiro-Silva A, Becker de Moura H, Ribeiro do Vale F, Zucoloto S. The differential regulation of human telomerase reverse transcriptase and vascular endothelial growth factor may contribute to the clinically more aggressive behavior of p63-positive breast carcinomas. Int J Biol Markers 2005;20(4):227-34.

37. Stewart GL. Trichinella and Trichinosis Plenum Press, 1983.

38. Despommier DD, Laccetti A. Trichinella spiralis: proteins and antigens isolated from a large-particle fraction derived from the muscle larvae. Exp. Parasitol. 1981;51:279-295.

39. Despommier DD. The worm that would be virus. Parasitol. Today 1990;6:193-195.

40. Borkow G, Bentwich Z. Chronic Immune Activation Associated with Chronic Helminthic and Human Immunodeficiency Virus Infections: Role of Hyporesponsiveness and Anergy. Clin. Microbiol. Rev. 2004;17(4):1012-103.

41. Borkow G, Bentwich Z. Chronic Immune Activation Associated with Chronic Helminthic and Human Immunodeficiency Virus Infections: Role of Hyporesponsiveness and Anergy. Clin. Microbiol. Rev. 2004;17(4):1012-1030

42. Pozio E. New patterns of Trichinella infection. Veterinary Parasitology 2001;98(1-3):133-148.

43. Gajadhar AA, Gamble HR. Historical perspectives and current global challenges of Trichinella and trichinellosis. Veterinary Parasitology 2000;93(3-4):183-189.

44. Nockler K, Pozio E, Voigt WP, Heidrich J. Detection of Trichinella infection in food animals. Veterinary Parasitology 2000;93(3-4):335-350.

45. USDA ERS. Pork trade projections. International Agricultural Baseline Projections to 2005 USDA, 2002.

46. Gajadhar AA, Gamble HR. Historical perspectives and current global challenges of Trichinella and trichinellosis. Veterinary Parasitology 2000;93(3-4):183-189.

47. Dupouy-Camet J. Trichinellosis: a worldwide zoonosis. Veterinary Parasitology 2000;93(3-4):191-200.

6

PARASITIC PLUNDERING

Decimation of the Poison-Animal Eater

Key Terms: avian influenza, chronic disease, chronic immune activation, dyspnoea, edema, eosinophils, helminthes, infiltrates, influenza, longevity, myocarditis, neurotrichinosis, sequelae, small intestine, swine influenza, thromboembolic diseases, trichinosis, upper limits

From the outset, two critical points must be briefly addressed before taking up the destructive workings of poison-animal pathogens on human life. As with each preceding aspect of the perils associated with poison-animal, the Honorable Elijah Muhammad's simple truths in the books, *How To Eat To Live (books 1 & 2)*, serves as the premise for these points. The first point deals with the *upper limits* of human longevity — a concept that is unknown to the common masses of people. The second addresses the predominant cause of sickness and death in this world — a world contrary to the *ways of* and *mandates given* by Almighty God.

Poison-animal eaters put up a fight to justify eating poison-animal unlike none waged for other meats. The most popular argument used by such persons is "my grandmother ate pork and lived to be 80 years old". The poison-animal eater is presuming that 80 years is a standard of long life. This is far from the truth.

In the Bible, the accounts of how the human lifespan was cut short from hundreds of years to the mere 70 or 80 years many people reach today, are clearly described. The prophet David, in Psalms 90:1-10, confirms that living 70 years (or near that age) is the consequence of rebellion against Almighty God.

This does not mean that our relatives were not and are not good-hearted people. It means that they followed the only way of life they knew, which happened to be Satan's way of life, which is in direct opposition to the divine laws, rules and regulations of God — although our relatives professed belief in God.

We must keep in mind that the foreparents of the Black man and woman of America were enslaved and the lives they lived, right down to the religion they practiced, were taught to them by their enslavers. It is one thing to sing words of praise, but knowing how to live the life that the Creator intended for us to live is an entirely different thing, and the most difficult to do, particularly in this world.

We must be taught how to live a divine life because our enslavers did not teach us this nor did they know it themselves. Certainly, the Caucasian enslavers were not friends of the True God and could not truthfully claim to have known HIM, believed in HIM or worshipped HIM, yet these demons declared they were all these things. They epitomized arrogance and audaciousness to the fullest.

The world in which we live is built from this demonic mindset; therefore, we should not wonder why human suffering has engulfed the earth. Our disastrous existence under this satanic rulership is proof of this world's opposition against Almighty God, and the millions of churches operating around the country fall far short of proving otherwise.

LONGEVITY & DISEASE

The Honorable Elijah Muhammad writes in *How To Eat To Live, Book 2*:

> If Noah and Methuselah had heard you boasting that your parents lived only 75 or 80 years eating poison, they would have considered your parents as never having grown up to become adults, according to their good way of eating the best foods, about twice a week, and living nearly 1,000 years of our present calendar years which consist of 365 days.

Leading researchers in the field of geriatrics and longevity agree that humans can live longer than 70 to 80 years. Nevertheless, no mainstream researcher has ventured as far as stating that humans can live 200 or 300 years. Most of them consider 125 years as the upper limit.[1] Almighty God knows best. This world's scientific understanding of life is nothing compared to what HE knows, and what this world recommends in the way of health advice supports the pandemics of morbidity and early mortality. These facts are substantiated hourly.

The Honorable Elijah Muhammad emphatically confirms that we have the potential to live 200, 300, 400 or more years. Equally as important is that He also provides the means by which this can be accomplished. This is the way of God — HE shows us how to reach our full potential. This leads to the second point.

In Book 1 of *How To Eat To Live*, the Honorable Elijah Muhammad states:

> We must be careful of what we put in our stomachs because what we put in our stomachs will maintain life and it will take life away.

All health professionals agree with this simple law. For centuries disease has been linked to diet. Eating is required to sustain life; therefore, diet has a foremost role in determining both the quality and length of life. Even the unborn child has a dependency on the diet of its mother. The reality of the role of diet is not new, although many so-called health experts would like us to believe that they have stumbled onto something new.

The chronic disease pandemic comprises preventable diseases, making good dietary habits the foremost preventive measure. A good diet starts with the knowledge of the foods that God both recommends and forbids. As we know, humans are divinely-forbidden to eat poison-animal; nevertheless, government health experts, and many nutritionists and dieticians recommend eating this poison meat. This is a monumental evil in the name of science and medicine.

With eating poison-animal, the eater is both in direct rebellion against God, and is eating an animal that causes disability and death. The result is a lifespan between 40 and 80 years, rather than 200 and 300 years. To make matters worst, these few years are spent in agony from the afflictions caused by the infestation of the virulent pathogens harbored in poison-animal.

CLINICAL PATHOLOGY

The colossal pathogenic infestation of every organ in the body, as well as the parasites' conquest of the immune system equates to the complete physiological destruction, although gradual, of the poison-animal eater's life. Nearly every health ailment, illness or disease can reasonably be attributed to the consumption of poison-animal. In all practicality, this chapter can end on that statement; however, because many poison-animal eaters are unaware of the signs and symptoms of parasitic infections, it is prudent to cover these areas. This may inspire some people to stop eating this diseased meat after learning that they are experiencing the health conditions detailed in this and the chapters that follow.

DISEASE MANIFESTATION

The deceptively intelligent workings of parasites relegate scientists to merely assessing the clinical pathologies of the acute manifestations of infection. Most parasitic infections, however, are either mild or asymptomatic.

This reality is the rule when it comes to parasitic infections. Minor symptoms, however, are nearly always present in these infections but are often diagnosed as other ailments. The more severe infections may lend to an accurate diagnosis, if the doctor tests for parasites.

Consequently, most people do not know they are infected, and the gross misunderstandings regarding health and disease only lend to the problem. Here is the point — now that chronic disease is the order of the day, people have grown more accustomed to combating diseases than enjoying good health. And, despite these continuous health bouts, many people are not apt to consider that parasitic infections are the cause of their ailments. After all, who wants to think that they have millions of worms living in their bodies?

TRICHINELLA AS THE MODEL

As the most studied of the "superior" helminthes, the clinical aspects of Trichinella spiralis (T. spiralis) infection have been covered in depth. The physiological, biological and neurological damage caused by this parasite is a realistic model for the general workings of most helminthes and many other pathogens. For this reason, the disease pathologies caused by T. spiralis infestation are examined in this chapter.

The clinical manifestation of T. spiralis infection is called *trichinosis* or *trichinellosis*. This infection is characterized by acute and life-threatening complications.

INFESTATION PHASE-RELATED PLUNDERING

The plundering of the poison-animal eater's life is associated with identifiable parasitic infestation phases. These include *intestinal invasion, migratory, muscle invasion* and *calcification phases*. Each of these phases has immunologic implications, as the immune system is fundamentally involved in the entire infestation. Overall, inflammation is the hallmark of the immune system's response.

Although the infection process is phase-oriented, these phases coexist and meld because the poison-animal eater gets re-infected with every bite of poison-animal meat. For some people, re-infection occurs on an hourly basis, as poison-animal is eaten throughout the day – *from can't see morning to can't see night* – for decades. The destructive four-phase cycle is continuous and the assault on the poison-animal eater's life is constant.

The health consequences of each infestation phase are described in the following sections.

INTESTINAL INVASION PHASE

Trichinella parasites (and many other helminthes), after having been unleashed from their cysts in the stomach, advance to the intestine. There, they burrow deep into this organ and continuously copulate. Therefore, the first anatomical victim of T. spiralis infestation is the intestine. The mutilation of the intestinal lining or mucosa is a major injury that impedes digestive and other metabolic processes. This destruction is paramount, having far-reaching implications that are linked to many health ailments and diseases. The function of the intestine confirms this point.

For example, we have learned that the small intestine serves the primary purpose of further degrading and absorbing the nutrients the body requires to sustain life.

STOMACH, INTERNAL SURFACE

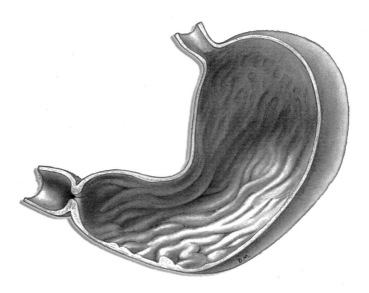

The gastric juices digest the parasitic cysts and unleashes the larvae. The fact that larvae can withstand these powerful and highly acidic juices proves that cooking poison-animal does not destroy all the pathogens contained in this flesh.

The small intestine is essential to the digestive process — as we can eat all the food we want, but if this food cannot be digested, then our efforts are in vain. Consequently, disease and early mortality eventually results due to the lack of nutrients required by the cells of the body.

This organ is also responsible for keeping foreign particles from entering the bloodstream and is a housing for immune cells that further sanitize the food material.

The intestinal lining is comprised of many different types of cells, such as epithelia, absorptive, goblet, and enteroendocrine cells, to name a few. These cells are vital to digestive and immunological functions. For example, enteroendocrine cells secrete hormones, such as cholecystokinin and gastrin, while goblet cells secrete lubricating mucus, and absorptive cells absorb water, which has the major role in digestive activities.

The destruction of the intestinal lining means the destruction of these cells, eventually leading to the organ's failure — a failing that occurs gradually, and is commensurable with the overall degeneration of the human vessel.

The destruction parasites cause to the small intestine has been well documented. While in the intestine, the parasites cause alterations in the cell epithelium; deformation of the villi; enterocyte proliferation at the villus margins, hyperplasis of the Crypts of the Lieberkuhn, and massive cellular infiltrates in the mucosal layer.[2] Infiltrates are immunological-generated substances that gradually accumulate in cells or body tissues, and are characterized as either isolated (focal) or broad (massive).

Villi are tissue projections into the lumen covered predominantly with mature, absorptive enterocytes and mucus-secreting goblet cells. The *Crypts (of Lieberkuhn)* are tubular invaginations of the epithelium around the villi, lined largely with the epithelial cells involved in secretion processes. At the base of the crypts are stem cells, which continually divide and serve as the foundation of the epithelial cells in the crypts and on the villi.

INTESTINE AND PANCREAS

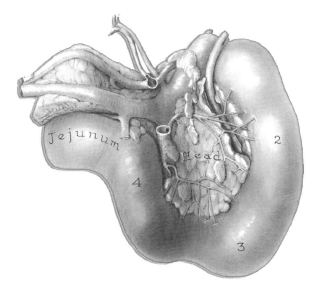

The parasite's destruction of the intestines leads to an enormity of acute and chronic ailments and diseases.

The destruction of this organ leads to digestive, metabolic and immunological problems. Digestive problems arise from interference with nutrition and metabolism, causing metabolic problems, such as diabetes mellitus. Immunological problems occur as many types of pathogens advance through a weakened intestinal lining and enter the bloodstream. Again, the intestine is also a line of protection and is supposed to prevent foreign substances from entering the bloodstream.

During the initial process of intestinal mutilation, most poison-animal eaters experience gastrointestinal symptoms such as upper abdominal pain, diarrhea or constipation, vomiting, malaise, and fever, all of which can vary in severity.[3] These conditions last from a few days to several weeks, especially during re-infection.

Clinically, these problems are characteristic of many intestinal disorders, such as food poisoning or indigestion, and are easily and often misdiagnosed. As a result, the common response of infected people is that they usually do not seek medical attention. They take one or more of the many digestive medicines on the market.

Some people experience abdominal discomfort so frequently that taking digestive medicines is a way of life. The pills or potions to relieve constipation, diarrhea, indigestion or abdominal pain accompany each meal. Sometimes these *nostrums* are placed beside the plate of food. These medicines may soothe the discomfort but the parasites' awesome infestation continues to ravage the body, unbeknown to the poison-animal eater.

MIGRATORY PHASE

The migratory phase starts when parasites leave the intestine and begin traveling the blood and lymphatic circulatory systems. The parasites' destination, as previously noted, is the muscle tissues, because their goal is to make homes in the muscles through the encapsulation and calcification processes. Along the way, these parasites cause disturbances, as they migrate through other tissues. A litany of health problems is associated with this phase.

Several important organs are distinctly affected by the migratory phase, specifically the heart and eyes.

INFECTION OF THE HEART

T. spiralis larvae are not known to encapsulate in the heart; however, their migration leads to alterations of heart tissues.[2]

These alterations are induced by lesions, which trigger a cascade of immunological responses that damage the heart. Studies have shown the presence of infiltrates, primarily eosinophils and mononuclear cells.

Although signs of infestation of the heart usually appear in the early stages of Trichinella infection, the migration through the organ is more extensive in the later periods, usually between the fourth and eighth week of infection. Heart pain and tachycardia occur in six to 22 percent of patients diagnosed with trichinosis. Tachycardia is a rapid heart rate, especially one above 100 beats per minute in an adult. Other symptoms, such as dull heart tones, heart murmurs, and arrhythmia occur.

In the late stages, severe infection with T. spiralis usually causes myocarditis[4] — both interstitial and eosinophilic. Myocarditis is the inflammation of the myocardium, which is the muscular tissue of the heart. Interstitial relates to the small and narrow spaces between tissues or parts of the organ. Substances lodging in these areas cause the heart to swell.

HEART AND GREAT VESSELS, STERNOCOSTAL VIEW

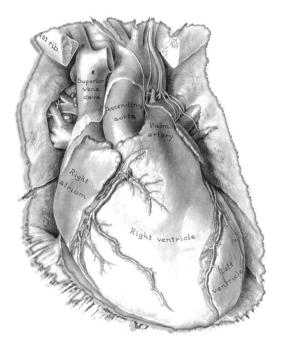

Migration of parasites through the heart leads to severe alterations of heart tissues, and subsequent, complications.

Eosinophils are one of many substances released in response to heart infestation. It is a type of leukocyte, and comprises one to three percent of the total white blood cell count. Eosinophils are known to aid against parasitic infections, and is a hallmark of infection. In the previous chapter we noted that the presence of eosinophils usually confirms that a parasitic infection exists. Inflammation ensues when eosinophils are present because these cells secrete chemical substances that cause swelling to occur.

Trichinella infection of the heart also causes noted granuloma formations, which are masses or nodules of chronically inflamed tissue. These formations represent the severe altering of the heart muscle.

Thromboembolic diseases also occur when parasites infect the heart. Conditions such as deep thrombophlebitis, intraventricular thrombi and pulmonary embolism usually occur.

Thromboembolism is the blocking of blood vessels by clotting, while thrombophlebitis is inflammation of veins caused by or associated with the formation of blood clots. These conditions can be fatal, as they restrict the flow of blood.

In addition, edema of the lower limbs from hypoalbuminemia – an abnormally low level of albumin in the blood – has been observed in association with cardiovascular complications. Albumin is a water-soluble protein that plays a role in controlling the coagulation of blood. When this substance is low, embolus develop, which are thickened particles. These particles circulate in the blood causing blood clots in veins and arteries. In severe cases of trichinosis, sudden death can result from embolism of the pulmonary artery.[5]

Overall, the parasites weaken the heart as they migrate through it, making heart failure highly likely. There is no doubt that parasites are part of the reason why heart disease has been the leading cause of morbidity and mortality in the last several decades and beyond.

INFECTION OF THE EYES

The eyes are another area where the migration of Trichinella registers substantial damage. Infection of the eyes is a cardinal feature of Trichinella infection. Typical symptoms of infection include edema within the conjunctiva, uvea, retina and optic nerves.

The poison-animal eater experiences pain when moving the eyeballs. In severe cases, paralysis of the muscles surrounding the eyes occur.

The migration of larvae causes lesions in the eye area, which disturbs microcirculation. Lesions to the retina occur as larvae migrate through the ciliary arterioles and the central artery of the retina. This leads to irreversible damage, with partial or complete blindness usually resulting.

ORBIT AND EYEBALL, ANTERIOR VIEW

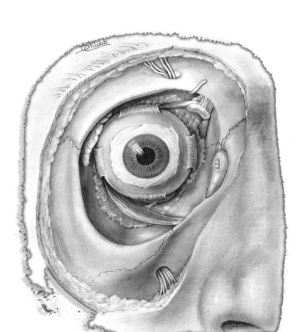

Parasites infest the eye areas, causing tissue damage. This leads to severe vision problems, including partial or complete blindness.

MUSCLE INVASION PHASE

According to parasitologists, both migratory and muscular phases are related to the acute manifestation of infection, as both lesions and cysts damage the internal organs. For most people, the onset of the acute stage occurs suddenly and manifest as symptoms that include weakness, chills, headache, fever, excessive sweating and tachycardia. Eyelid and periocular edema also occur.

Edema frequently affects the entire face. There are many poison-animal eaters that have enlarged faces on such a continuous basis that their faces remain this way. In fact, their entire bodies appear continuously swelled. This is different from what is seen in obesity and reflects the parasites' ability to deform the body. It also shows that the immune system is highly active due to the massive invasion of parasites throughout the body.

As covered in Chapter 5, the forming of cysts in muscles by parasites is known as the encapsulation process. Therefore, the muscle encapsulation phase is characterized by the distinct invasion of organs. Several organs that are chief targets of parasites control critical respiratory and neurological functions.

RESPIRATORY (BREATHING) HINDRANCES

Disturbances of the respiratory system are seen during both early and late stages of trichinosis. At the early stage of the disease, disturbances are related to the migration of larvae and responses by the immune system. A series of tissue alterations including hemorrhagic lesions, vascular thrombosis and cellular infiltrates (eosinophils and lymphocytes) around the perialveolar vessels occur. The alveolar pertains to the tiny air sacs of the lungs.

These adverse conditions often cause pneumonitis and bronchitis. Pneumonia is a common cause of death in parasitic infections.[6]

The following table lists the health ailments often associated with the indiscriminate penetration of larvae into tissues throughout the body.

Main clinical and biological features of human trichinosis

Features	% of Frequency in Outbreaks	Length
Clinical (symptoms and signs)		
Diarrhea and flatulence	0-40%, 100% for Trichinella nativa	1-7 days (up to 3 weeks)
Abdominal pain	6-60%	1-7 days
Loss of appetite	70-85%	2-4 weeks
Vomiting	5-10%	1-2 days
General weakness	85-97%	1-4 weeks
Headache	80-90%	2-3 weeks (up to 5 weeks)
Fever (up to 40^0C)	41-100%	1-2 weeks
Excessive sweating	45-60%	1-2 weeks
Eyelid of limbs	6-8%	5-7 days
Periocular edema	17-100%; 0% for Trichinella nativa	5-7 days
Eye pain upon ocular movement	77%	5-7 days
Facial edema	43-88%	5-7 days
Edema of limbs	6-8%	5-7 days
Cutaneous rash	4-51%	3-5 days
Petechiae	2-12%	2-4 days
Intraconjunctival hemorrhages	56-73%	3-5 days
Hemorrhages of nail beds	49-65%	3-5 days
Myalgia	59-97%; 25-60 for Trichinella nativa	2-3 weeks
Myocarditis	5-20%	1-2 weeks
Neurological complications	3-60%	2-4 weeks
From Clinical Aspects, Diagnosis and Treatment of Trichinellosis.[6]		

In Chapter 5, we learned that the discovery of the Trichinella parasite came from the study of a cadaver that had the parasites lodged in the victim's diaphragm. This revealed a severe respiratory condition.

Infestation of this organ causes a condition known as *dyspnoea,* which is marked by shortness of breath, coughing, hoarseness, and overall difficulty in breathing.[7] Death is the eventual result of this respiratory infection.

INNERVATION OF LUNGS, ANTERIOR VIEW

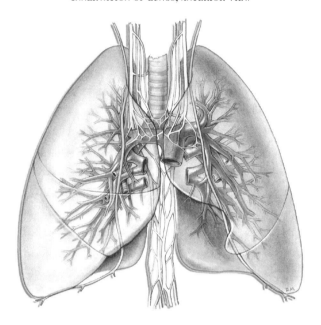

Parasites infest the muscle areas responsible for breathing. The lungs are a primary target of Trichinella parasites and its infestation leads to respiratory failure

NEUROLOGICAL DAMAGE

In the book, *How To Eat To Live,* the Honorable Elijah Muhammad described the pathology of Trichinella infection. He writes:[8]

> They first enter the walls of the stomach and then from the stomach pass out into the intestinal walls. And, from the intestines they travel up the back in the spinal cord into the muscles of the body and finally into the brain. When these worms get into these two places, last mentioned (of the body), the disease becomes incurable.

This pathology differs from the dominant perspective regarding Trichinella's pattern of invasion. In the previous chapter, we noted the popular view from this world's scientists — that Trichinella travels the blood vessels and "lymphatics" to reach striated muscle areas. Researchers know that this parasite ultimately infects the brain area, but are baffled by how this is achieved.

The Honorable Elijah Muhammad indicates that the spinal cord or fluid is the means by which Trichinella infection spreads to muscles and the brain. The parasites use the lymphatics and blood vessels to reach the spinal fluid.

This means that neurological affects begin shortly after infection. Therefore, seeing this parasite in the muscles means that neurological damage has occurred and is continuously underway. The ultimate goal of this parasite is to infect the brain. Even parasites strive to gain ultimate control of their hosts by invading the area where all control lies.

Neurological manifestations of trichinosis occur in 10 to 24% of diagnosed cases. Brain infection from this parasite is known as *neurotrichinosis*. This disease has also been the subject of much research.

In one study, 55 patients affected by neurotrichinosis had meningoencephalitic signs (96%), followed by focal paralysis or paresis (73%), and delirium (71%).[9] Psychosis was also evident among those infected.

In the paper, *Neurologic Manifestations in Trichinosis*, the following is detailed:[10]

> Several pathogenic mechanisms are responsible for the neurological complications in trichinosis: obstruction of brain blood vessels by larvae, cysts or granulomas, toxic vasculitis with secondary thrombosis and haemorrhages, granulomatous inflammation of the brain parenchyma and allergic reaction.

Generally, the parasites' penetration of cerebral tissue causes severe infection of the nervous system. Clinical conditions include meningitis, encephalitis, polyradiculoneuritis, poliomyelitis, myasthenia gravis, paresis and paralysis. These are extremely grave conditions.

For example, poliomyelitis is described:

> A highly infectious viral disease that chiefly affects children and, in its acute forms, causes inflammation of motor neurons of the spinal cord and brainstem, leading to paralysis, muscular atrophy, and often deformity. Also called infantile paralysis.

These serious ailments testify to the Honorable Elijah Muhammad's words that the *disease becomes incurable* when infection reaches the spine and brain.

SPINAL CORD IN SITU, POSTERIOR VIEW

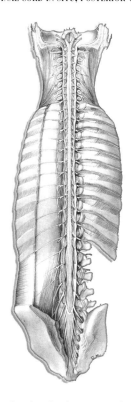

Parasites travel the spinal cord and make their way to the brain. When parasites infect the neurological system, the diseases they cause are incurable.

We can assume that the incidence of undiagnosed neurotrichinosis is substantially higher than known cases. In fact, it is safe to say that such cases are pandemic because anyone eating poison-animal has neurological infections on some level. Medical professionals may diagnose these infections as other ailments, but if people who ate poison-animal obtained examinations for parasitic infections, most would be surprised by the findings — emphatically confirming they have parasites throughout their bodies. Of course, the Medical Profession already knows this.

ENCYSTED RESTING LARVAE — CALCIFICATION

Trichinella's encapsulation in the muscles is usually manifested two weeks into the infection and completed within five weeks,[11] depending on the Trichinella species involved.[12] In humans, the calcification process begins about five months after infection and is usually completed after 18 months.[11] Again, in Chapter 5, we learned that the calcification process completely and permanently alters the infected muscles.

Pain and the continued disruption of the immune system are trademarks of the parasite's encasement process. The poison-animal eater experiences pain in extraocular (eye area) muscles, masseters, tongue and larynx muscles, diaphragm, neck muscles, and intercostal muscles. The masseters are thick muscles in the cheek that closes the jaw during chewing. Intercostal muscles are situated between the ribs.

These muscles become stiff, hard, and edematous.[13] Some poison-animal eaters have experienced pain that is so severe that normal functions such as walking, speaking, breathing, and swallowing are severely restricted. Poison-animal eaters are often stricken with weakness because of the additional energy required to perform basic muscle movements, and infestation of the thoracic cavity inhibits their ability to breathe properly.

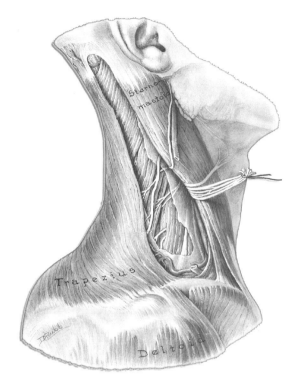

Parasites encapsulate in muscles around the shoulders and neck. Many poison-animal eaters experience chronic pain in these areas.

CHRONIC CONDITIONS

The clinical pathology of Trichinella infection demonstrates the parasite's ability to endure in the poison-animal eater's muscles and tissues for as long as the person lives, and even beyond that. Notwithstanding, few studies have been conducted to determine the long-term or chronic implications of T. spiralis infection. This subject has been somewhat controversial among health professionals because of the alleged difficulty in identifying post-trichinosis effects from chronic forms of infections.[14]

The studies that have been conducted have been confined to the *sequelae* from acute infections. Sequelae are pathological effects or ailments resulting from a disease. It is the ongoing affects of infection.

No studies have been conducted to show the implications of chronic infections in undiagnosed cases, yet this knowledge holds more weight when it comes to parasitic or pathogenic infections than do acute infections. This is because there are far more people with undiagnosed infection than are those with diagnosed infections. This is in keeping with the subversive workings of parasites and viruses.

In considering chronic parasitic infections, we must examine what we know about the infestation of T. spiralis, whether the symptoms are acute, mild or asymptomatic. We know that encysted larvae persist in muscles throughout the body. We also know that the immune system continues high alert activities because this is required for T. spiralis' larvae to survive in their nurse-cells. Moreover, we know that by continuing to eat poison-animal, the poison-animal eater is continuously battling parasitic infestation.

In studies of the "persisting sequelae"[15] of chronic trichinosis, the health ailments often noted included persistence of myalgia, early fatigability, ocular signs, and headache. These conditions lasted decades after infection. Some recent studies have confirmed the occurrence of these ailments for periods up to 10 years after recovery from *diagnosed* trichinosis.[16]

In the research paper, *Clinical Aspects, Diagnosis and Treatment of Trichinellosis*, the following is stated:

> ...there have been reports of people who, months or even years after the acute stage, continued to suffer from chronic pain, general discomfort, tingling, numbness, and excessive sweating, and who showed signs of paranoia and a syndrome of persecution.

In the previous chapter, we learned that nurse-cell formation permanently alters the muscle tissues. This means that escaping pain is unlikely. Infections of the brain also produce permanent alterations of brain tissue; thereby, causing permanent mental derangement. This substantiates the fact that advanced Trichinella infection is incurable. At best, the pain can be managed, but the destruction has already occurred and usually continues.

Clinical studies of 44 patients – one, three, four, six and seven years after experiencing trichinosis – confirmed the continuance of various general and motor ailments experienced by nearly 89 percent of the patients.[17] Also, the persistence of antibodies against Trichinella antigens was evident in 86 percent of patients. This confirmed that chronic stimulation of the immune system by the larvae continued long after acute infection.

These findings are aligned with another study that confirmed the persistence of immune responses against Trichinella in patients that had, years prior, suffered trichinosis.[18] This condition is also described as *chronic immune activation*, and is associated with chronic helminthic infections.

A comprehensive article on this subject noted:[19]

> Chronic immune activation is one of the hallmarks of human immunodeficiency virus (HIV) infection. It is present also, with very similar characteristics, in very large human populations infested with helminthic infections...Not surprisingly, several of the immune derangements and impairments seen in HIV infection, and considered by many to be the "specific" effects of HIV, can be found in helminth-infected but HIV-noninfected individuals and can thus be accounted for by the chronic immune activation itself.

The subject of chronic immune activation has a significant bearing on the chronic disease plight in these modern times. As stated above, the opportunistic infections that are familiar occurrences in HIV infection are also frequent in parasitic infections. Yet, how readily do we hear parasites mentioned as the cause of popular ailments such as rheumatism, diabetes mellitus, thyroid conditions, heart disease and cancer?

The long-term health conditions arising from acute infections are not always life threatening. Few deaths are associated with acute infections. Non-acute infections, at best, register mild symptoms. This issue has already been addressed. In addition, those diagnosed with trichinosis have probably banned poison-animal from their diets, while those unaware of the infection continue to eat this flesh, which makes their conditions progressively worst.

Therefore, we can surmise that the chronic ailments experienced after acute infection are the same as those of undiagnosed infections. In one sense, undiagnosed infections might be worse because the poison-animal eater is not only unaware of the infestation, but also has not taken interventions, such as drugs, to fight the parasites, as are people diagnosed with trichinosis.

CHRONIC BRAIN DAMAGE

Regarding the brain, studies confirm that the central nervous system's involvement in trichinosis is not uncommon.[20] Multifocal lesions located in the cerebral cortex and white matter have been identified in both acute and chronic infections.

CEREBRAL HEMISPHERE, DISSECTION, LATERAL VIEW

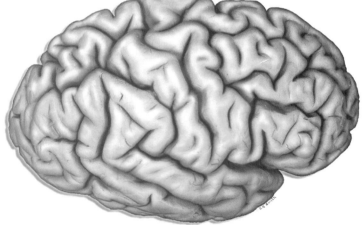

Trichinella and other brain parasites cause long-term chronic infections by infecting the brain tissues. Parasites are responsible for several commonly known neurological diseases.

The most feared of all viruses have been those that cause influenza, and the reasons are understandable. The influenza virus outbreaks of 1918, 1957, and 1968 caused the deaths of tens of millions of people throughout the world. Since 1968, numerous, but more isolated, outbreaks have occurred. The most recent was in 2004, when a highly pathogenic *avian influenza A (H5N1)* virus broke out among poultry operations in eight Asian countries — affecting dozens of people and killing 32 of them.[21] Even without occurrences of isolated epidemics or pandemics, approximately 36,000 people in the United States (U.S.) die each year from influenza or the "flu".

Influenza is a respiratory infection with classic symptoms that include fever, coughing, and muscle aches, and which usually lasts a few days. According to virologists, the viruses are not the cause of the pneumonia that sometimes lead to death, but the viruses weaken the immune system, and consequently, exposes the person to infections by other pathogens that cause respiratory failure.[22]

Influenza is thought to be a natural infection of aquatic birds; hence, the term avian influenza. However, as with many viruses, infection can be transmitted to other hosts, particularly mammals. These infections can be transitory or established.[23]

Established viruses wreck havoc on animal and human populations. Influenza viruses have been isolated from swine, horses, poultry and humans. The viruses that caused the major influenza pandemics were various strains of avian, swine and human viruses.[24]

Generally, viruses are known for their ability to change in molecular structure, making it difficult to effectively vaccinate against or intervene in viral infections. The influenza viruses are known to change their H and N hemagglutinin molecule terminals. These changes lead to new strains and make current antibiotics or vaccines ineffective. For example, a swine influenza virus is slated as the cause of the 1918 influenza pandemic. This virus was labeled H1N1. Other strains were later identified, such as H2N1 and H2N2. Since 1998, the H3N2 virus has been identified in poison-animal throughout U.S. farms.[25]

For scientists, understanding how viruses change their molecular structures has been complicated and difficult, lending to the mystery surrounding the workings of influenza viruses. However, scientists do know that new viruses are developed by the recombination of viruses from different hosts. For example, influenza viruses from poison-animal, birds and humans mix to form new strains of viruses.

These new forms are the most dangerous, and have the potential to cause major pandemics, which has occurred on several occasions, particularly with the outbreaks of 1957 and 1968.

The new H3N2 virus presently infecting the U.S. poison-animal populations is a *triple reassortant* containing avian-like, swine-like, and human-like gene segments. Overall, scientists have identified approximately 15 strains of influenza viruses.

POISON-ANIMAL INFLUENZA TO HUMAN

Considering the diseased nature of poison-animal, there is no doubt that it harbors influenza viruses. There is also no doubt that these viruses are transferred to humans when people come in contact with poison-animal. This is well known.

On the other hand, the ability for avian influenza viruses to infect humans has been controversial. The traditional belief was that bird-to-human transmission was not possible. Other researchers have challenged this position, and posit that the occurrence of H5N1 and H9N2 viral infections among people in Asia from 1997 to 1999, proves the potential for avian influenza viruses to directly infect humans.[26] This debate continues.

The poison-animal has long been known to act as an intermediary for interspecies transmission.[27] In the research paper, *Serologic Evidence of H1 Swine Influenza Virus Infection in Swine Farm Residents and Employees,* this point is confirmed:

> ...but direct avian-to-human transmission of influenza viruses is a rare event. In contrast, the species barrier for transmission of influenza viruses between people and pigs appears to be less stringent, and influenza virus infections in pigs pose important public health concerns at two levels.

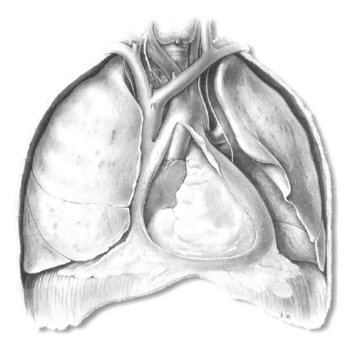

Both parasites and viruses infect the areas of the lungs, causing severe respiratory problems. Pneumonia is a leading cause of death in parasitic infections of the respiratory tract.

The poison-animal serves as a "mixing pot" for both avian and human viruses, and is the chief means for the transmission of influenza to the human population; hence, the swine influenza outbreaks among the human population. This fact calls our attention to another aspect of the poisonous nature of this animal — its ability to serve as a live laboratory for the genetic engineering of many kinds of pathogens.

Within this divinely-forbidden animal, scores of parasites, bacteria, viruses and fungi continuously mix and match genes to manufacture new forms of virulent pathogens. This sheds light on why it is impossible to purify this animal. The rightness of the divine mandate against eating this beast is also substantiated. Eating this meat puts the poison-animal eater on death row. This is a fact.

Unfortunately, whether intentional or unintentional, U.S. researchers have chosen to make much ado about the threat of an avian influenza pandemic rather than a swine influenza pandemic. This position has evil written all over it and is a clear demonstration of this world's demented and grossly evil satiation for profits, at the expense of human life.

The mention or warning of a possible swine influenza outbreak would lead to significant reductions in the sales of poison-animal meat. The merchants of death labor intensively to make sure the population remains blind to this truth.

Human infection with swine influenza viruses is a common reality and studies continuously show this to be a growing threat.[27] For example, a landmark study examined multiple swine-exposed human populations in the nation's top swine-producing state, for evidence of swine influenza infections.[28] Researchers performed controlled, cross-sectional seroprevalence studies among 111 farmers, 97 meat processing workers, 65 veterinarians, and 79 control subjects using serum samples collected between 2002 and 2004.

The samples were tested against six influenza (A-type) virus isolates, which comprised various H1N1, H1N2, and H3N2 viruses, collected from poison-animal and humans. The results confirmed that all three exposed groups – farmers, meat processing workers and veterinarians – had markedly elevated *titers* against the H1N1 and H1N2 swine influenza virus isolates, compared with controlled subjects. The researchers reported:

> Farmers had the strongest indication of exposure to swine H1N1 virus infection followed by veterinarians and meat processing workers. Similarly, farmers had the highest odds for exposure to swine H1N2 virus followed by veterinarians and meat processing workers. Occupational exposure to pigs greatly increases workers' risk of swine influenza virus infection. Swine workers should be included in pandemic surveillance and in antiviral and immunization strategies.

Clearly, it comes as no surprise that those working at poison-animal farming facilities are infected by poison-animal pathogens. However, Chapter 8 shows the vast detrimental effects of poison-animal industrial farming on surrounding ecosystems, and draws attention to the spread of swine influenza viruses through sadistic industrial farming practices. The poison-animal farming industry has made environmental conditions suitable for influenza pandemics. This, too, has not been communicated to the public.

MORE THAN THIS

T. spiralis is one of 999 pathogens that live in poison-animal, yet the destruction it levies against the poison-animal eater is monumental. What about the destructive affects of the other 998 germs? All these germs infest the bodies of those who eat this divinely-forbidden flesh.

By now, it should be clear how we lose decades of life by eating this poisonous meat. This is why Almighty God forbids us to eat it.

REFERENCES

1. S. Jay Olshanky BAC, and Christine K. Cassel. In Search of Methuselah: Estimating the Upper Limits to Human Longevity. Science 1990;250(November 2):634-40.
2. Kociecka W. Trichinellosis: human disease, diagnosis and treatment. Veterinary Parasitology 2000;93(3-4):365-383.
3. Pawlowski Z. Clinical aspects in man. In: Campbell W, ed. Trichinella and trichinosis. New York: Plenum Press, 1983;367-01.
4. Kirchhoff L, Weiss L, Wittner M, Tanowitz H. Parasitic diseases of the heart. Front Biosci 2004;9:706-23.
5. Kocicka W. Trichinellosis: human disease, diagnosis and treatment. Vet. Parasitol 2000;93:365-383.
6. Pozio E, Gomez Morales M, Dupouy-Camet J. Clinical aspects, diagnosis and treatment of trichinellosis. Expert Rev Anti Infect Ther 2003;1(3):471-82.
7. Compton S. Trichinosis with ventilatory failure and persistent myocarditis. Clin Infect Dis 1993;16:500-04.
8. Muhammad E. How To Eat To Live. Vol. 2. Chicago, IL: FCN Publishing Company, 1972.
9. Dalessio D, Wolff H. Trichinella spiralis infection of the central nervous system. Arch Neurol 1961;4:407-17 1961;4(407-17).

10. Nikolic S, Vujosevic M, Sasic M, Poluga J, Misic S, Najdanovic L, Dulovic O, Dragojlovic J, Milosevic B. Neurologic manifestations in trichinosis. Srp Arh Celok Lek. 1998;126(5-6):209-13.

11. Gould S. Anatomic pathology. In: Gould S, ed. Trichinosis in man and animals. Springfield, IL: Charles C Thomas, 1970;147-89.

12. Pozio E, La Rosa G, Rossi P, al. e. Biological characterizations of trichinella isolates from various host species and geographical regions. J Parasitol 1992;78:647-53.

13. Aldrige F. An outbreak of trichinosis in Pennsylvania. Am J Med Sci 1931;181:312-23.

14. Fröscher W, Gullotta F, Saathoff M, al. e. Chronic trichinosis. Clinical, bioptic, serological and electromyographic observations. Eur Neurol 1988;28:221-6.

15. Kassur B, Januskiewicz J, Poznanska H. Controversial aspects in human trichinellosis. In: Kim C, Ruitemberg E, Teppema J, eds. Trichinellosis. Chertsey: Reedbooks, 1981;245-7.

16. Feldmeier H, Biensle U, Janssen-Rosseck R, al. e. Sequelae after infection with Trichinella spiralis: a prospective cohort study. Wien Klin Wochenschr 1991;103:111-6.

17. Kociecka W, Bombicki K, Pielok L, Gustowska L. New aspects of clinical pathology and electro-physiological muscle disturbances in patients with history of trichinellosis. Parasite 2001;8((2 Suppl)):S173-5.

18. Bruschi F, Locci M, Cabaj W, Moskwa B, Castagna B, Kociecka W, Masetti M. Persistence of reactivity against the 45 k Da glycoprotein in late trichinellosis patients. Vet Parasitol 2005;132(1-2):115-8.

19. Borkow G, Bentwich Z. Chronic Immune Activation Associated with Chronic Helminthic and Human Immunodeficiency Virus Infections: Role of Hyporesponsiveness and Anergy. Clin. Microbiol. Rev. 2004;17(4):1012-1030.

20. Gelal F, Kumral E, Vidinli B, D E, Yucel K, Erdogan N. Diffusion-weighted and conventional MR imaging in neurotrichinosis. Acta Radiol 2005;46(2):196-9.

21. Ungchusak K, Auewarakul P, Dowell SF, Kitphati R, Auwanit W, Puthavathana P, Uiprasertkul M, Boonnak K, Pittayawonganon C, Cox NJ, Zaki SR, Thawatsupha P, Chittaganpitch M, Khontong R, Simmerman JM, Chunsutthiwat S. Probable Person-to-Person Transmission of Avian Influenza A (H5N1). N Engl J Med 2005:NEJMoa044021.

22. Silverstein AM. Pure Politics and Impure Science: The Swine Flu Affair. Baltimore and London: The John Hopkins University Press, 1981.

23. Lipatov AS, Govorkova EA, Webby RJ, Ozaki H, Peiris M, Guan Y, Poon L, Webster RG. Influenza: Emergence and Control. J. Virol. 2004;78(17):8951-8959.

24. Monto AS. The Threat of an Avian Influenza Pandemic. N Engl J Med 2005:NEJMp048343.

25. Richt JA, Lager KM, Janke BH, Woods RD, Webster RG, Webby RJ. Pathogenic and Antigenic Properties of Phylogenetically Distinct Reassortant H3N2 Swine Influenza Viruses Cocirculating in the United States. J. Clin. Microbiol. 2003;41(7):3198-3205.

26. Olsen C, Brammer L, Easterday B, Arden N, Belay E, Baker I, Cox N. Serologic evidence of H1 swine Influenza virus infection in swine farm residents and employees. Emerg Infect Dis 2002;8(8):814-9.

27. Ayora-Talavera G, Cadavieco-Burgos J, Canul-Armas A. Serologic evidence of human and swine influenza in Mayan persons. Emerg Infect Dis 2005;11(1):158-61.

28. Myers K, Olsen C, Setterquist S, Capuano A, Donham K, Thacker E, Merchant J, Gray G. Are Swine workers in the United States at increased risk of infection with zoonotic influenza virus? Clin Infect Dis 2006;42 Epub 2005 Nov 22(1):14-20.

29. Choi Y, Lee J, Erickson G, Goyal S, Joo H, Webster R, Webby R. H3N2 influenza virus transmission from swine to turkeys, United States. Emerg Infect Dis 2004;10(2):2156-60.

7

Sounding the Mental Power

Brain Disease-Causing Parasites

Key Terms: blood-brain barrier, cerebrospinal fluid, cryptogenic epilepsy, cysticericosis, epilepsy, etiology, eukaryotic, evolutionary, hydrocephalus, immune system, intracranial hypertension, mental retardation, morbidity, mortality, neurocysticercosis, parasitologists, genetic predisposition, seizure, Taenia solium, Toxoplasmic gondii, Trichina spiralis

W e start this chapter revisiting *Problem No. 9* of *The Problem Book*, in *The Supreme Wisdom*:

It is known to the Medical Profession and other wise Muslim Sons that poison-animal sounds the mental power; one-sixtieth of an ounce per every ten ounces of poison-animal. If the average person contains seven and one-half ounces of brain, then Mr. Muhammad wants to know how long will it take to sound the seven and one-half ounces at the above eating rates.

The average person can be robbed successfully with one-third of unsound brain. Then how long will a Devil have to wait to rob of said, the poison-animal eater, at the above rates?

Without doing the math, we can agree that the wait is not that long. One reason is that peoples' life spans are not that long, so the robbery must commence as soon as possible. In addition, poison-animal eaters pass the detrimental affects to their offspring because some parasites are capable of infecting the unborn child. This usually occurs through the reproductive organs.

This is a very important subject because too often the concept of "predisposition" is relegated to genetics — that is, we are predisposed to the diseases our parents suffered before or during our births. Few medical scientists, particularly those in industrialized countries, take up the issue of generational parasitic infections, and how this "predisposition" is far more common and far more debilitating than alleged genetic predispositions.

As previously stated, during the chattel slavery era, Caucasian physicians recommended that slave owners, who wanted well nourished slaves, feed their captives pork. The following words epitomize the sadistic arrogance through which such a demented recommendation came:[1]

> ...fatty articles of diet are peculiarly appropriate on account of their heat producing properties' and 'fat back and pork are the most nourishing of all foods for the negro.

This recommendation to feed poison-animal to enslaved Black people under the auspices of good nutrition was intended to destroy our brain power, readying us to be mentally enslaved after the physical shackles were taken off our wrists and ankles.

Our deplorable condition proves that we have been mentally numbed. What is the reason for this? Part of the reason is best expressed in the book, *Racism, Health, and Post-Industrialism:*[2]

> ...certain dysfunctional cultural habits are very difficult to alter because they frequently are reinforced by the system of exploitation.

Our continuous consumption of poison-animal meat is tied to the wealth of America's so-called healthcare system, and various other sectors of society that profit from our misery, by reason of our *sounded* brains and overall moral and physical debilitation.

Poison-animal is sold everywhere throughout the Black community. Death-dealing merchants exploit us through our ignorant traditions, and we are foolish for continuing to give credence to practices that were forced on us while in chattel slavery. Each generation passes on traditions of poor dietary habits, which glorifies the eating of the worst creatures that can be taken as food — under the banner of "soul-food".

ABOUT THE BRAIN

For the sake of getting on common ground, we define the brain as follows:

> The portion of the vertebrate central nervous system that is enclosed within the cranium, continuous with the spinal cord, and composed of gray matter and white matter. It is the primary center for the regulation and control of bodily activities, receiving and interpreting sensory impulses, and transmitting information to the muscles and body organs. It is also the seat of consciousness, thought, memory, and emotion.

Most of us consider the brain and the heart to be the two most important organs in the body. Now that people have lived a few days with artificial hearts and no one has made an artificial brain, the brain reigns supreme as the most important organ. It is also highly unlikely that a machine can be made to perform functions remotely close to that which the brain does.

The importance of the brain is apparent in the protection given to it in the makeup of the human body. No other organ is protected quite like the brain. The skull protects it from external injury. Internally, the brain fluid keeps it suspended in water to cushion it from hitting against the skull.

Unfortunately, human behavior shows that we do not place the same value on the brain as the Creator did and does. Sports, such as boxing, football and other suicidal games, cause brain injuries galore. In addition, people eat anything and everything, including a multitude of foods that harm the brain. Generally, our ignorance, recklessness, carelessness and outright rebellion are the chief causes of brain damage.

Most of us know that damaging the brain alters its function. The most severe damage causes the brain to cease from functioning in a way where the victim is considered brain-dead. Usually a machine keeps the heart and other vital organs working, but the brain has lost its ability to regulate and control these organs, as well as life-sustaining activities.

CRANIAL FOSSA, POSTERIOR, BONY FEATURES

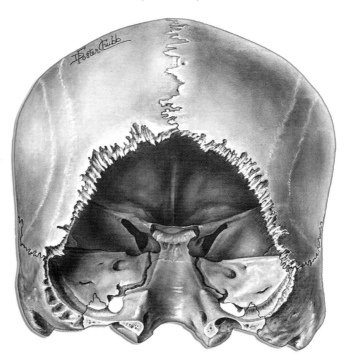

The brain is the most protected organ in the body, which establishes it as the most important organ in the body. While the skull protects the brain from external injury, our intelligence and wise eating habits are required to protect it from internal injury.

Less severe injuries have rendered people disabled in varying degrees. Some people cannot speak, see or hear as they once did. Others have trouble moving about and properly performing life's activities. Some cannot think clearly or accurately — their sense of awareness and ability to calculate time and space are disrupted. Still, others have lost their ability to reason. Generally, these people are classified as mentally disabled or impaired.

The term *sound* in the context of *Problem No. 9* is synonymous with the phrase *to deaden,* which means:

> To make vague or obscure or make less visible; Cut a girdle around so as to kill by interrupting the circulation of water and nutrients; Make vapid or deprive of spirit; 4) lessen the momentum or velocity of; and, Become lifeless, less lively, intense, or active; lose life, force, or vigor.

A person experiences all these ordeals when eating poison-animal. By what means does eating poison-animal sound or deaden the poison-animal eater's brain?

In spite of the fact that we are living in the 21st century, most people do not know that the poison-animal is a repository of parasites, viruses, bacteria and fungi of an enormously dangerous sort. Again, these things make it a poisonous animal.

The threat associated with eating this divinely-forbidden meat is two-fold. First, scientists have not been able to identify the extent of the poison in this animal. The Honorable Elijah Muhammad states that the *hog* is 999 percent poison. This world's scientists cannot comprehend what it means for something to be 999 percent poisonous. Since 1835, when the Trichinella parasite was discovered in poison-animal, they have attempted to do so, but have fallen way short.

Government agencies, health associations and other entities have issued recommendations for eliminating specific parasitic threats; however, they are not knowledgeable of the extent of the poison in this animal. How can they make such a recommendation on miniscule knowledge? This leads to the second factor.

Although scientists have isolated and identified several virulent disease-causing parasites in poison-animal, they are still at a loss in understanding how these parasites circumvent the immune system, and launch an extended assault on the poison-animal eater's life. Such an assault is characterized by the parasites' invasion of nearly every organ in the body, including the brain.

Therefore, not only do they lack knowledge about the vastness of the parasites that infect swine, they also do not know the extent of the damage these pathogens cause. Of course, not knowing the magnitude of the damage, disallows effective treatment.

BRAIN-DESTROYING PARASITES

The body, innately, does not let just anything enter the brain area, and rightly so — it is the most important organ in the body. The brain has a blood-brain barrier, which is comprised of cells that prevent unwanted substances in the bloodstream from entering the brain. This is similar to the way the intestinal lining is charged with keeping unwanted particles from entering the bloodstream.

OVERVIEW OF BRAIN AND VENTRICLES

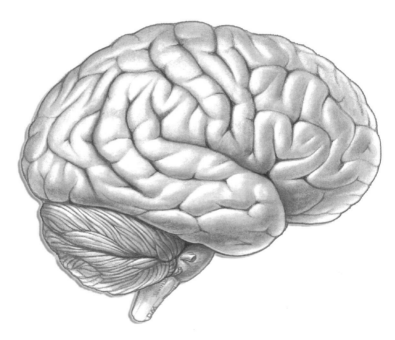

The brain is the ultimate target of many parasites. Parasites lodge in the brain and destroy the brain cells and circuitry, causing a litany of ailments to occur.

Parasites can eventually overrun this barrier, and once they do, they have to contend with the immune system, which is another difficult task. Yet, they overcome that, too. This is what makes parasites fierce opponents of human life. Basically, parasites must *invade* the body and *evade* the immune system to survive. These are their primary challenges.

A parasite's battle ground is always the immune system. Therefore, they possess an intelligence that is evolutionary, revolutionary and highly adaptable. This intelligence works to ensure not only that they survive, but also thrive. This is why people do themselves a grave disservice when they take chances by eating meats put on the market by sadistic food industries.

The most studied of several parasites that cause brain damage are *Trichina spiralis, Taenia solium* and *Toxoplasmic gondii.* These parasites are extremely formidable and the way they go about infecting those who eat poison-animal and other meats that harbor them, continues to baffle parasitologists and other scientists.

Each of these parasites successfully cross the blood-brain barrier, circumvent the immune system and establish themselves in the brain; thereby *sounding* it. Scientists have learned that parasites access the brain by releasing antigens and enzymes that dissolve areas of the blood-brain barrier. In fact, all tissues are permeated by parasites through the use of these substances. If parasites can penetrate the most protected organ in the body, then the other organs do not stand a chance. This is precisely the case.

No mammal – human or otherwise – is on record as having been able to effectively defend itself against these "super" parasites. The only sure preventive measures are not eating poison-animal and other meats known to harbor them, and avoiding environmental conditions having high risks of pathogenic infections. Other preventative recommendations, especially those that offer guidance about cooking this diseased meat, have failed.

Just the same, no medicine or potion has effectively treated severe parasitic infections. In short, these worms enter the body easily when given the opportunity, but getting them out of the body is next to impossible.

The following section describes how *Taenia solium* orchestrates its invasion of the human brain.

WORM WORKINGS

••

Taenia solium (T. solium), also known as the *pork worm*, is one of the most common brain disease-causing parasites, infecting millions of people worldwide.[3] Again, the common person is unaware of this. In fact, it is safe to say that most people are unaware that brain parasites even exist.

T. solium parasites, also called cysticerci, cause an infection known as *cysticercosis*. This infection causes many debilitating conditions. Death is also associated with severe infections.

When consumed by the poison-animal eater in its larval stage, this parasite latches to the intestine. There, it can thrive and grow to be several feet in length. However, when the cysts (eggs) are eaten, they hatch in the stomach via the action of gastric acid. The larvae then make their way through the intestine and enter the bloodstream where they eventually travel to the brain. Along the way, they wreck havoc on other organs of the body, as the parasites invade subcutaneous tissue, eyes, muscles, heart, liver, and lungs.

With respect to the brain, this parasite is the leading cause of brain diseases, especially epilepsy. Parasites can remain in the brain for a long time because the cysts are protected by both the blood-brain barrier and immune system, which combine to prevent drug therapies, such as anthelminthics, from effectively treating the infection. T. solium cysts can be active for many years before they begin to degenerate.[4]

When the cysticerci reach the brain, they attach to either the brain tissue itself, or to cavities through which brain fluid flows. In each case, grave conditions result. Once attached, the larvae develop into large cysts, producing the disease known as *neurocysticercosis*.

The location of the cysts determines the symptoms exhibited by the poison-animal eater. When the larvae attach to the brain tissue, the infected person usually experiences frequent and debilitating seizures. This occurs, in part, because the presence of the cysts interferes with the electrical activity of the brain, causing it to become uncontrollable.

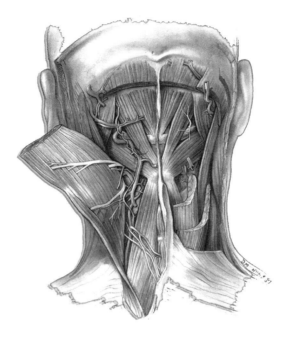

Parasites make their way up the spine and enter the brain area. Once in this area, the diseases they cause become incurable.

Seizures are defined:

> Attacks of cerebral origin consisting of sudden and transitory abnormal phenomena of a motor, sensory, autonomic or psychic nature resulting from transient dysfunction of the brain.

On the other hand, if the larvae attach to the brain-fluid cavities, the poison-animal eater experiences headaches, nausea, dizziness, and altered mental states, as well as seizures. These additional effects are caused by blockage of brain fluid.[5] Consequently, the brain cells are cannot receive the required nutrients nor effectively eliminate waste.

In addition, the presence of the larvae causes the lining of the brain-fluid cavities to become inflamed. This further constricts the flow of brain fluid, causing increased cranial pressure. In response, the heart pumps harder, as an attempt to deliver the much needed nutrients to the brain. This is the working of the body's biofeedback system. The heart's effort, however, only increases the pressure in the brain.

If this condition is not treated, brain cells begin dying and major brain damage occurs due to both the pressure on the brain and its inability to receive required nutrients.

Both conditions are usually featured in neurocysticercosis, as cysts form in both the brain tissues and cavities. Again, once the parasites enter the brain, they can lodge anywhere in the brain. The entire brain is at their disposal.

The immune system also reacts when the cysts begin degenerating. Cyst degeneration causes the parasite to lose its ability to dodge the immune system. Because the immune system is now able to recognize these invaders, it attacks them. It also responds to the damaged brain tissues.

These reactions cause inflammation, which often results in permanent damage to brain tissues.[6] The majority of acute and chronic cases of neurocysticercosis are the direct result of the inflammatory process that accompanies cyst degeneration.

PAIN OF BRAIN-SOUNDING

Neurocysticercosis is a syndrome marked by epilepsy, intracranial hypertension, and hydrocephalus. As previously stated, parasitic cysts disturb the electrical activity of the brain, causing brain seizures to occur.

The latter two conditions – intracranial hypertension and hydrocephalus – are directly related to the blockage of brain fluid in the cavities (cerebral ventricles or basal cisterns) by parasitic cysts.

The following sections provide brief overviews about each of these conditions.

EPILEPSY

Epilepsy is a common condition of the central nervous system that causes unpredictable and recurrent seizures. A seizure occurs from a brief, uncontrolled electrical discharge by the nerve cells of the brain. During a full seizure, a person's consciousness, movements, and actions are markedly altered. The person usually experiences convulsions; falls to the ground unconscious, while having a stiffened body and making jerking movements.

INTRACRANIAL HYPERTENSION

This condition is characterized by extensive pressure within the skull, which appears along the paths of the optic nerves, causing the nerves to swell (papilledema). If untreated, permanent or temporary blindness ensues.

The most common symptom of this condition is an unbearably painful headache that is usually difficult to relieve, even with medication. Other common symptoms include transient altered vision, intracranial noise (pulse synchronous tinnitus), stiff neck, back pain, double vision, and pain behind the eyes.

HYDROCEPHALUS

The word "hydrocephalus" means water (hydro) and head (cephalus). This condition is an accumulation of brain (cerebrospinal) fluid in the ventricles of the brain, causing swelling of the brain. Brain fluid usually circulates ventricles in the brain and spinal canal. When the circulation or absorption of this fluid is blocked, the volume of fluid in the brain is excessively increased. This accumulation puts pressure on the brain, damaging and destroying brain cells.

Symptoms of hydrocephalus vary depending on the cause of the obstruction and the extent of brain damage due to swelling; however, typical characteristics include enlargement of the head, prominence of the forehead, brain atrophy, mental deterioration and convulsions.

TOXOPLASMIC GONDII EPILEPSY

Let us briefly turn our attention to Toxoplasmic gondii (T. gondii) and how this parasite causes epilepsy.

T. gondii is a complex eukaryotic that infects many cell types of a wide range of animal species. This ability has made it one of the most prevalent parasites worldwide. The parasite causes a broad spectrum of diseases.

Most infections, however, are mild or asymptomatic. This means the person is not acutely aware of the infection. Here, we are reminded of the Honorable Elijah Muhammad's words *deceitful poison*, regarding how parasites work.

T. gondii is also known to lodge in muscles and tissues surrounding the eyes. This parasite causes a disease known as *toxoplasmosis*. Common symptoms include enlarged neck lymph nodes, malaise, muscle pains, enlarged lymph nodes, and enlarged glands. Other less common symptoms include anemia, liver symptoms, low-blood pressure, blood symptoms, eye symptoms, and eye inflammation.

One study indicated that T. gondii is a leading cause of cryptogenic epilepsy.[7] This classification applies to e*pilepsy syndromes for which an etiology is unknown, but an underlying brain disease is suspected*. In this study, 75 percent of the 22 patients with cryptogenic epilepsy had elevated T. gondii antibody levels, compared to 22 others who did not have epilepsy (controls).

The study suggested that 20 percent of the American population is infected with T. gondii. As with T. solium, this parasite is found in poison-animal meat earmarked for human consumption.[8]

Clinical manifestations of brain toxoplasmosis include encephalitis, chorioretinitis, pneumonitis and myocarditis. Symptoms may include global encephalitis, with altered mental status (75%), focal neurological deficits (70%), headache (50%), fever (45%), seizures (30%), weakness, and cranial nerve abnormalities.

Conventional diagnostic testing, such as MRI and spinal fluid analysis are often unable to detect parasitic cysts in the brain. These cysts are usually found only when sections of the brain are removed during surgery for epilepsy treatment. This, of course, means that many brain infections go undiagnosed.

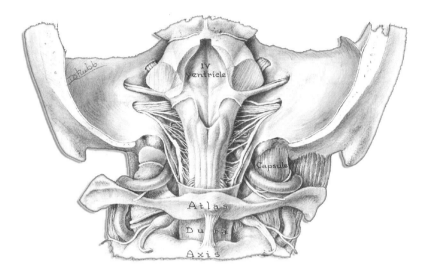

MIDDLE CRANIAL FOSSA

When parasites ravage the brain, they cause pressure to develop in the cranial area by restricting the flow of blood and brain fluid, and by occupying space in the brain. This leads to conditions such as epilepsy, hydrocephalus and intracranial hypertension.

PREVALENCE OF BRAIN-SOUNDING

Each year, billions of people eat poison-animal. Therefore, it comes as no surprise that parasite-related brain damage is pandemic.

WORLD-WIDE INCIDENCE

The World Health Organization estimates that approximately 50 million people are infected with the T. solium parasite, making both cysticercosis and neurocysticercosis common diseases. These infections are endemic in the Andean area of South America, Brazil, Central America and Mexico; China, the Indian subcontinent and South-East Asia; and sub-Saharan Africa.[9]

Up to one-third of the world's population is infected with T. gondii.[10]

UNITED STATES

Neurocysticercosis is a growing public health problem in the United States. Among Hispanic populations, neurocysticercosis accounts for 13.5 percent of emergency room visits for seizures. Epidemiological data show that cysticercosis is a known cause of death among Hispanics living in California.[11]

Although no study of neurocysticercosis among Black people has been conducted, epilepsy is an emerging condition in Black America. To date, epilepsy is estimated to affect 350,000 Black people,[12] and approximately 24,000 are diagnosed with this condition each year.

Overall, seizures and epilepsy affects 2.3 million Americans, with 181,000 new cases occurring each year in the United States.[13] Proportionately, Black people make up a significant segment of epilepsy incidence. This is a common occurrence with other chronic ailments, and these conditions point to diet as a major contributing factor.

The few epidemiological studies assessing racial distribution of epilepsy indicate that this disease is 1-5- to 2-fold higher in Black people (African Americans) of all ages, compared to the general population, and from 1.1- to 1.4-fold higher when children are compared.

A study conducted with residents living in northern Manhattan demonstrated higher racial and ethnic disparities in the incidence of unprovoked seizures and epilepsy. Rates among Black people exceeded those of Caucasians by factors of 6.4 and 2.4 for children and adults, respectively. Similarly, rates among Hispanics exceeded those among non-Hispanics by factors of 2.1 for children and 1.7 for adults.

Although seizures begin at any age, they most often occur in children and elderly people. However, adult-onset seizures are outpacing these segments. "Onset" refers to diseases or chronic ailments that are in the early stages of development, and gradually become full blown over a period of time. This is how diseases from bad dietary or lifestyle habits often arise.

BRAIN, BASE/CEREBRAL ARTERIAL CIRCLE

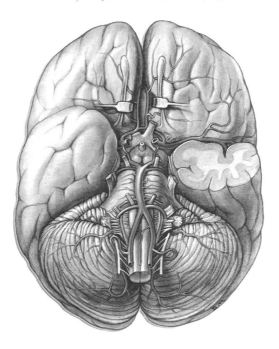

Parasites severely disturb the brain's electrical network, causing conditions such as epilepsy.

ULTIMATE ROBBERY

Some health writers claim that epilepsy, even when caused by brain disease-causing parasites, does not lead to mental retardation or mental illness. We can only wonder how they arrived at this conclusion. With large cysts lodged in a person's brain, causing disarray in the electrical circuitry and bloating of the brain, how can a person not experience some level of psychological, emotional, and physical instability, on an enduring basis?

According to other researchers, 26 percent of children with mental retardation have epilepsy; 37 percent of children with epilepsy also suffer from mental retardation; and 50 percent of people with mental retardation and cerebral palsy have epilepsy.[13] The incidence of epilepsy is related to the severity of intellectual impairment.

This means that there is no doubt that epilepsy chronically affects the brain. The rate of epilepsy is approximately 20 percent in persons with mild intellectual impairment, but can be as high as 50 percent in those with severe-to-profound intellectual disability.

Medical and quality-of-life costs, as well as morbidity and mortality costs, associated with epilepsy are enormous. For example, recent estimates reveal that hospitalizations account for 50 to 60 percent of the healthcare costs, with antiepileptic drugs accounting for 20 to 30 percent.[14]

People with active seizures use about two to three times more healthcare services than those whose seizures are controlled, and the costs to them and to society increase with each increment in seizure frequency. The total costs are five times higher for those with active seizures. In addition, the costs associated with work productivity and home life are the bulk of the total costs.[15]

The mortality rate among people suffering epilepsy is also mind-boggling. These persons have a mortality rate two to three times higher than the rest of the population. In addition, the risk of sudden death is 24 times that of the general population; and sudden-unexpected-death in epilepsy (SUDEP) is responsible for two to 17 percent of deaths of people with epilepsy.[16]

DOING THE MATH

Although information about the brain disease-causing parasites reveals the destructiveness of eating poison-animal, the sounding of our brains through eating this diseased meat goes beyond this.

Problem 9 of *The Problem Book* calls our attention to the mathematical precision of the brain destruction caused by eating poison-animal. Again, we revisit this Equation:

> ...poison-animal sounds the mental power; one-sixtieth of an ounce per every ten ounces of poison-animal. If the average person contains seven and one-half ounces of brain, then Mr. Muhammad wants to know how long will it take to sound the seven and one-half ounces at the above eating rates.

This knowledge represents a great offering from Almighty God, in the Person of Master Fard Muhammad. HE gives us an opportunity to contemplate, analyze and "do the math" so that we can assess our own self-destruction coming through the consumption of this divinely-forbidden meat. As such, HE brings us face-to-face with the realities behind the illnesses and diseases we suffer. No longer are we justified in believing that disease "just happens". Nothing happens without an action — whether intentional or unintentional.

We must consider the fact that the rulers of this world have a stake in sounding our brains, because the wealth they receive from effectively robbing us is enormous. The mere fact that poison-animal is sold by the millions, while knowing that virulent pathogens persist in this animal is evidence that something diabolical is taking place.

REFERENCES

1. Wilson. The Negro - His Diet, Clothing, etc.
2. Semmes CE. The Challenges of Post-Slavery Rural and Urban Life. Racism, Health and Post-Industrialism: A Theory of African-American Health. Westport, CT: Praeger, 1996;53.
3. Manzo A. Brain Worms and Brain Amoebas: They Do Exist. Engineering & Science 2003;4:32-36.
4. García HH, Gonzalez AE, Evans CAW, Gilman RH. Taenia solium cysticercosis. The Lancet 2003;361:547-556.
5. Note: In addition to providing cushion, as previously mentioned, brain fluid carries nutrients and waste to and from the brain.
6. Restrepo BI, Alvarez JI, Castano JA, Arias LF, Restrepo M, Trujillo J, Colegial CH, Teale JM. Brain Granulomas in Neurocysticercosis Patients Are Associated with a Th1 and Th2 Profile. Infect. Immun. 2001;69(7):4554-4560.
7. Stommel EW, Seguin R, Thadani VM, Schwartzman JD, Gilbert K, Ryan KA, Tosteson TD, Kasper LH. Cryptogenic Epilepsy: An Infectious Etiology? Epilepsia 2001;42(3):436-438.

8. Secretariat. Control of neurocysticercosis: Report by the Secretariat. Fifty-sixth World Health Assembly World Heath Organization, 2003.

9. DeGiorgio C, Pietsch-Escueta S, Tsang V, Corral-Leyva G, Ng L, Medina M, Astudillo S, Padilla N, Leyva P, Martinez L, Noh J, Levine M, del Villasenor R, Sorvillo F. Sero-prevalence of Taenia solium Cysticercosis and Taenia solium Taeniasis in California, USA. Acta Neurol Scand 2005;111:84-88.

10. USA E. Epilepsy in African Americans: Facts and Figures. Vol. 2005 Epilepsy Foundation, 2004.

11. Hill D, Dubey J. Toxoplasma gondii: transmission, diagnosis and prevention. Clin Microbiol Infect 2002;8(10):634-640

12. Society AE, Prevention TCfDCa, Directors CD, Foundation E, Centers NAoE. Report of the 2003 National Conference on Public Health and Epilepsy: Priorities for a Public Health Agenda on Epilepsy. In: Barkley GL, ed. The Living Well with Epilepsy II. Landover, MD: Epilepsy Foundation, 2003.

13. Alvarez N. Epilepsy in Adults with Mental Retardation. eMedicine.com 2005.

14. Begley CE, Famulari M, Annegers JF, et al. The cost of epilepsy in the United States: an estimate from populationbased clinical and survey data. Epilepsia. 2000;41:342-351.

15. Ramsay RE, Pryor F. Epilepsy in the elderly. Neurology. 2000;55(suppl 1):S9-S14.

16. Ficker D. Sudden unexplained death and injury in epilepsy. Epilepsia. 2000;41(suppl 2):S7-S12.

...OR TOUCH THEIR CARCASSES

Perils of the Poison-Animal Industry

Key Terms: ammonia, anaerobic lagoon, bacteria, carbon dioxide, carcass, commercialization, confined animal feeding operation (CAFO), Cryptosporidium, effluent, environmental injustice, excreta, hydrogen sulfide, methane, overapplication, parasite, pathogen, quintile, slurry pit, virus

M uch has already been explained about why poison-animal is an abomination or kanzir and hazir — *the foul, and the most unclean and the most abhorred of all animals.* The previous chapters addressed many aspects associated with the perils of eating this foul beast, with only a Scriptural mention that we are also forbidden to touch it. No doubt, there are afflictions associated with having this nasty, filthy and poisonous animal living among us.

These afflictions are 1000-fold, because this animal is a food commodity. Commercialization makes matters worse, as greed blinds the greedy to the destruction caused by their callous pursuit of profits.

This particular aspect of the divine law – that is, being forbidden to touch poison-animal – opens an important issue concerning the need for this beast in these modern times. If we take the law of God at heart, which we should and must do, then not being permitted to touch poison-animal means that this beast is no longer required to serve the purpose for which it was made.

As we have learned, poison-animal was made for medical purposes. This happened about 4,000 years ago. Since that time, medical science has advanced to the extent that this way of treating illnesses, using a foul beast, is no longer necessary. Ironically, the devouring of poison-animal at breakfast, lunch and dinner is driving healthcare expenditures through the roof — as eating that which was genetically-manufactured to serve medical purposes, has spurred the need for thousands of medications. Albeit, to no avail, especially for those who continue to eat this disease-causing meat. Eating this meat keeps the medical industry a foremost profit center.

ENVIRONMENTAL DESTRUCTION

Many people are unaware of the environmental destruction and human affliction caused by raising and marketing poison-animal. The following is stated in the handbook, *Controlling Odor and Gaseous Emission Problems from Industrial Swine Facilities:*[1]

> In the tight confines of these buildings, swine become soiled with manure, urine and feed dust, their body heat radiating the odor of the culmination of these substances. In most large-scale facilities, the manure and urine that do not collect on the swine pass through slatted floors into a holding area beneath the building, where they remain until the next removal date.

According to some environmental assessments, the horrendous stench coming from these confinement houses generate 35 percent of the odor associated with massive commercial poison-animal productions. The other areas of industrial poison-animal facilities that contribute to this funk include waste storage (20%); land application practices (40%), which involve the liquefying of this waste and then using it as crop fertilizer; and carcass disposal (5%).

Although only 5 percent is given for carcass disposal, the smell of any dead animal is most unbearable. This becomes more unbearable when this is a dead animal that already has the most horrible odor when alive. The contribution of carcasses to the stench arising from these facilities is considerable.

Disease, crowding, and other mass production techniques used in industrial poison-animal facilities contribute to the unintended death of thousands of animals each month. For example, a poison-animal facility of 1,000 animals typically produces about 40,000 pounds of dead animals per year. Most large poison-animal operations have tens of thousands of animals, so the poundage of dead carcasses is hundreds of thousands.

With profit at stake, the thought that meat from these dead animals may still enter the marketplace is realistic. Consumers should not underestimate the level of evil that is borne from an inordinate satiation for profits. Perhaps the sentiment of the sinister merchants that may do this is that a dead poison-animal cannot be anymore poisonous than a living poison-animal, despite the way the animal died — unintended or slaughtered.

POISON-ANIMAL INDUSTRY'S EXPLOSIVE GROWTH

A research article by the Federal Reserve Bank of Kansas City titled, *This Little Piggy Went to Market: Will the New Pork Industry Call the Heartland Home?*, describes the explosion of the poison-animal industry in the United States:

> Most analysts agree that the structure of the U.S. pork industry will soon resemble that of the U.S. poultry industry, which moved to a supply chain structure more than three decades ago. In short, the hog industry, once a quintessential family farm enterprise, has gone to market – a very big market.

This forecast has been fulfilled. In the 1990s, small family-owned farms dominated the United States' (U.S.) poison-animal industry. These farms, on average, raised several hundred animals. The marketing of poison-animal meat was more localized. However, as with America's entire agriculture spectrum, corporate greed – aided by bogus and deceptive government laws – captured these smaller poison-animal operations, eventually creating enormous agri-business establishments.

According to the U.S. Department of Agriculture, in 1982, there were 175,284 poison-animal farms containing 6.3 million animals; however, by 1997, the number of farms had plunged to 63,723 — a 64 percent drop.[2] On the other hand, the number of animals on the remaining farms increased to 8.2 million. The decrease was attributed, in part, to buyouts by major corporations. In addition, many farms were driven out of business through competition or malicious business dealings.

Although this was unfortunate for the small family farmer, this takeover did not sadden righteous people because anyone farming poison-animal is in violation of divine law. Nonetheless, the environmental pollution caused by industrial agri-business is dreadful compared to the small operations.

The mission of big agribusiness was to increase the sale of poison-animal across the globe. The overall goal was and remains to make poison-animal available to every person on earth. This, unfortunately, has nearly been achieved. According to the World Trade Organization, *pork is the world's meat of choice, representing 47 percent of daily meat protein intake in the world.* Individually, beef and poultry represent less than 30 percent of the daily global protein intake.[2]

American poison-animal producers have seized this previously untapped market. The U.S. is now among the global leaders of pork meat, exceeding 60 million units (individual animals) annually. This means that there is a poison-animal for every five U.S. citizens. The rate at which this animal is bred is phenomenal.

In keeping with contemporary business trends, a handful of mega-industrial poison-animal companies handle the majority of poison-animal production in the U.S. Smithfield Foods, Inc., Premium Standard Farms, and Prestage Farms are among the leading industrial poison-animal producers.[3] They operate large-scale facilities in states throughout America.

These large-scale enterprises are known as *confined animal feeding operations* (CAFOs). These facilities allow for high animal densities on relatively small land areas. Sadistic, inhumane, and dangerous practices are inherent in this type of business operation. Animals are packed into confinement houses, where their entire existence – from conception to birth, to slaughter to packaging – takes place.

Thousands of animals are packed into confinement houses, where their lives are managed from conception through slaughter.

Many poison-animal CAFOs process tens of thousands of animals each year. The sordid conditions in these facilities are mind-boggling, and their destructive impact on the surrounding communities is very apparent.

The humongous poison-animal operations in North Carolina have created stenches that span hundreds of miles in certain parts of the state. People living miles away from these facilities can smell the odor. Trucks carrying poison-animal by the hundreds move up and down the roads and highways stretching this pungent odor to other localities.

The northern states are not free from the effects of industrial poison-animal farming. Thousands of animals are imported from Canada, a big supplier for many U.S. companies. Truckloads of animals make their way southbound, creating a trail of ungodly odor.

OVERWHELMED BY EXCRETA

Vast amounts of poison-animal feces are produced in CAFOs. These animals produce two to five times the amount of waste than that of humans. A typical CAFO, containing 10,000 animals, produces a volume of "dooky" equal to that produced by a city of 25,000 or more humans.[4] Overall, livestock factories generate approximately 2.7 trillion pounds of manure each year, which must be managed without threatening the human population. What does 2.7 trillion pounds of feces look like? Merely considering this gives rise to the thought that managing this amount of waste is impossible.

Some environmentalists have estimated that 100 million tons of feces and urine are produced annually by the millions of poison-animal raised in the United States.[5] Poison-animal feces, however, is like no other manure. The multitudes of pathogens that infect poison-animal also pass in the feces. Therefore, poison-animal waste contains parasites, fungi, viruses, and bacteria.

In confirming the obvious, an assessment conducted by federal health investigators found harmful bacteria and other pollutants commonly associated with poison-animal feces in waterways and wells near several industrial poison-animal operations in Iowa.[6]

The enormous amount of poison-animal waste is unmanageable. This is a well-known fact, although some companies claim to have effective management practices. Both environmentalists and advocates of the poison-animal industry have offered proposals aimed at effective waste management.[7] These are worthless efforts. Nastiness is the very nature of this poisonous beast, and anyone remotely believing that this filth is manageable is far removed from reality.

In attempting to manage poison-animal excreta, most industrial poison-animal operations use *slurry pit systems* or *anaerobic lagoon systems*. Slurry systems store undiluted, untreated excreta in watertight tanks or pits until this waste is applied to the land.[8] Storage can be located under or outside the confinement house. However, many pits are located underneath the facility. The stored slurry is applied to fields by several means — sprayed; incorporated into the soil with chisel plows behind nurse tanks; or injected it directly into the soil with drag hoses.

Anaerobic lagoons or cesspools are the most popular waste storing systems.[8] Various kinds of anaerobic bacteria metabolize poison-animal excreta. Anaerobic bacteria do not use oxygen; therefore, they decompose organic matter more efficiently than aerobic bacteria.[9] Lagoons are popular because organic matter can be stabilized, and there is a reduction in the amount of waste. In addition, some of the diluted lagoon liquid is used to flush the confinement houses. This method, however, produces large quantities of ammonia.

WHITETAIL HOG FACILITY (MISSOURI)

Shallow retaining lagoon
Where manure sits before
being sprayed on
surrounding fields

More hog barns
and lagoons

Hog barns
(1 site of 9 with 8,832
hogs per site)

Aeration basin
Where manure goes after
the lagoon

20 million gallon
manure "lagoon"

This is a common breakout of many industrial poison-animal facilities.
Courtesy of http://www.factoryfarm.org/resources/photos/hogs/7-02.php

The resulting anaerobic decomposed waste is called *effluent*. This waste is aerosolized and applied to crop fields under the auspices of irrigation. The aerosolized waste drifts into areas many miles from the fields and settles in surface waters, homes, and humans. Of course, this is not management. This is the criminal act of making the lives of those living in surrounding communities intolerably difficult.

The unhealthy impact of living among poison-animal is exemplified in many studies on the horrific impact industrial poison-animal operations have on the surrounding environment and communities. One study, *Environmental Injustice and the Mississippi Hog Industry,* described the injustices associated with the selection of communities for large-scale poison-animal operations:[10]

> Some citizens of the state feel that corporate swine operators are adversely affecting their health and the vitality of their communities. Research has shown that industrial pork production may cause environmental health problems for ecosystems.

As is always the case, industries that cause significant damage to the environment and threaten the quality of human life are established in communities where most of the residents are either poor or Black. Those "classes" having political clout are always in a position to say "not in my backyard". However, the poor have no voice; therefore, the merchants of disease and death – a.k.a. industrial poison-animal enterprises – run roughshod over these communities, with no fear of legal recourse. This is precisely the case with poison-animal operations in Mississippi, North Carolina, and Iowa, which are major hubs for the poison-animal industry.

The environmental destruction and human health toll are calculable. These facilities emit noxious gases; and toxins from the decomposing feces in lagoons, spray-fields, and other sites severely contaminate the environment. The authors of the paper further state:

> Some of the environmental contaminants emitted into the atmosphere include ammonia, hydrosulfide, volatile organic compounds, particulates, and other pollutants.

Other researchers have identified several other gases that threatened human health. For example, industrial poison-animal operations produce four main types of gases linked to many environmental and human health problems. In addition to hydrogen sulfide and ammonia, the other two include carbon dioxide and methane. These gases are emitted from all four major components in industrial poison-animal facilities — confinement buildings, waste storage and treatment processes, land application practices, and carcass disposal areas.

Exposure to elevated levels of gases have caused health conditions ranging from mild irritation to death, in both poison-animal and human populations.[11] Many a poison-animal meet their demise through inhaling the toxic gases they generate. This sheds light on the high risks of disability and death to humans living near these facilities.

The following sections briefly describe the impact of these gases on the environment.

HYDROGEN SULFIDE

Hydrogen sulfide is the most toxic gas emanating from poison-animal facilities.[11] It is also called *hydrosulfuric acid, sewer gas,* or *stink damp.* This gas is heavier than air, inflammable, colorless and has a distinct odor of rotten eggs. It can be detected at low levels.

As previously noted, this gas is produced by the anaerobic decomposition of poison-animal excreta; and because it is soluble in water, it accumulates in underground pits and other low-lying unventilated areas.

Hydrogen sulfide poisoning usually occurs by inhalation. All organs are affected; however, the nervous system is most affected. High levels of exposure to this gas causes acute intoxication, which manifest in various symptoms including sudden fatigue, headaches, anxiety, loss of olfactory senses, nausea, sudden loss of consciousness, optic nerve dysfunction, hypertension, pulmonary edema, coma, seizures and severe respiratory distress, often followed by cardiac arrest and death.[12]

In the agriculture industry, this gas is the leading cause of most manure-related deaths of both humans and animals.[13]

CARBON DIOXIDE

Carbon dioxide is a natural gas produced from the respiratory processes of mammals. We inhale oxygen and exhale carbon dioxide. This gas also results from the decomposition of poison-animal excreta, namely the metabolizing of organic acids and carbohydrates found in the excreta. This is usually the most abundant gas generated from poison-animal excreta.

Carbon dioxide is not a highly toxic gas; however, high levels of exposure cause respiratory problems, eye irritation and headaches. It also acts as a narcotic at high exposure levels. Extremely high levels can cause asphyxiation, because this gas dilutes the oxygen content of the air. Exposure at these levels can kill humans and animals within a few hours.

AMMONIA

The ammonia gas in poison-animal feces also results from the decomposition process. According to the Environmental Defense Fund, over 80 percent of nitrogen in poison-animal manure is vaporized as ammonia.[14] This makes ammonia poisoning a foremost problem of industrial poison-animal operations.

Since 1991, ammonia levels have risen approximately 25 percent each year, paralleling the explosive growth of the poison-animal industry. Some researchers have estimated that poison-animal excreta lagoons in North Carolina pump nearly 200 tons of ammonia into the air each day.[13]

This gas rises in the environment and then returns to the earth by way of rain and fog. The gas is usually transformed into dry particles that can travel as far as 250 miles. Traces of urea, a byproduct of urine and feces, have been detected in the North Carolina rainfall.

Ammonia toxicity causes adverse human health conditions that span from mild to severe, and the corresponding affects range from eye irritation to death. Exposure to high levels of ammonia affects the skin, eyes, throat, and lungs, causing burns to these organs. Lung damage and death are associated with very high exposure.

METHANE

Methane is produced in both the digestive tract and during the excreta decomposition process; however, the methane emitted in the environment predominantly comes from excreta. This gas is highly combustible, making it very dangerous, especially in high temperature conditions. Methane is also dangerous because it is colorless, odorless, and tasteless, so it is very difficult to detect. At high levels of exposure, this gas causes asphyxiation.

WATER CONTAMINATION

Water is foundational to life. One would think that water would be the last thing anyone would want to pollute. Not so, with the poison-animal industry, which contaminate both surface and groundwater. This occurs through leakages in lagoons and runoffs from fields sprayed with liquid poison-animal excreta.[15]

A study in North Carolina found severe seepage of nitrogen from more then 50 percent of the lagoons tested by the state. This placed the groundwater at risk of contamination.[16]

Another study conducted by the Centers for Disease Control and Prevention (CDC) assessed the environmental impact of nine large poison-animal facilities in Iowa.[17] The study confirmed the presence of chemical pollutants, metals, bacteria, nitrates, and parasites in lagoons and other areas in and around the sites. The findings confirmed that both chemical pollutants and microbial pathogens move through soil from the lagoons to areas miles; thus polluting nearby communities.

Poison-animal farming is a treacherous act, and the treachery is elevated by the premeditated contamination of the land and water surrounding these large-scale facilities. Attempts to rid these facilities of the high volumes of poison-animal excreta have led to corruption and criminal acts. The merchants of death that operate poison-animal facilities often saturate the fields with this so-called manure fertilizer. This abusive act is called *over-application*, and is a common practice in poison-animal farming.[18]

DEAD POISON ANIMAL CARCASSES

Poison-animal die by the hundreds at CAFOs producing an unbearable stench and contaminating the surrounding environment.

The high cost of transporting excreta relative to the selling value of this pathogen-infested waste makes evil-doing attractive, with overapplication being the way out. A 1998 study indicated that 82 percent of industrial poison-animal facilities were overapplying excreta.[19] This crime is much worst today. As is often the case in this mad world, the pursuit of profit is preferred over human life.

Another study conducted in Missouri found 150 sites where poison-animal feces were routinely being over-applied to the fields.[4] The fields were saturated, causing the excess to run off into streams and waterways. There was evidence that this poison also leached into aquifers.

The overapplication of poison-animal excreta also destroys the soil. Studies conducted in two North Carolina counties revealed that 75 to 100 percent more nitrogen was being applied to fields than can be utilized by crops.[16]

When considering the pathogenic content of poison-animal feces used as fertilizer, the thought arises about the safety of the crops being grown and the contribution that these activities lend to the pandemic of disease that has gripped America. The industrial poison-animal operations contaminate the environment and food supply, making diseases from pathogens and toxic pollutants the most common experience in all of our lives.

The Honorable Elijah Muhammad reminds us that *this world* is absolutely opposed to life in every respect. The evil mindset dominating the corporate rulers is characterized by the desire for big mansions; expensive vehicles; fur coats; yachts; and an overabundance of wealth to live extravagantly. They care nothing about the destruction of the environment and its death-dealing affect on the current population, as well as forthcoming generations.

This so-called luxury is only enjoyed for a few decades, as most of these villains die around the age of 60 or 70 years, yet the damage they exact on the environment and the human family to enjoy this short span of luxury is extensive. This is a satanic mindset, and many of the persons owning and managing these corporations have so-called higher learning degrees from American colleges and universities.

HUMAN ILLNESSES

The occupational health hazards associated with working at industrial poison-animal facilities are enormous. We can simply state that any adverse effects experienced by those living in neighborhoods surrounding these facilities are in no *way*, *shape*, or *form* equal to what the workers experience.

These confinement buildings are clouded with dust particles consisting of poison-animal skin cells, feces, feed, bacteria, and fungi. Consequently, poison-animal workers experience a litany of health problems.

The research paper, *Concentrated Swine Feeding Operations and Public Health: A Review of Occupational and Community Health Effects,* provides an overview of typical health ailments experienced by both poison-animal industrial workers and people living near these production facilities:[21]

These symptoms are consistent with symptoms reported by CAFO workers: a) respiratory effects such as inflammation of the bronchi or bronchioles, wheezing, and cough (associated with air pollution, chronic agricultural dust inhalation, endotoxins, and smoking); b) nausea, weakness, dizziness, and fainting (associated with endotoxin exposure); c) headaches and plugged ears (25% of poison-animal workers have chronic sinusitis); and, d) runny nose, scratchy throat, and burning eyes (associated with exposure to irritant gases such as ammonia) at highly intense levels.

As the Honorable Elijah Muhammad states in the books, *How To Eat To Live* — the fact that people can handle and devour poison-animal is beyond righteous imagination. That anyone could work in industrial poison-animal facilities is also beyond imagination. Working in a poison-animal industrial facility is the same as working in a toxic waste dump. Therefore, living near these facilities is like living near toxic waste dumps.

Even with this being an obvious reality, companies are able to goad communities into accepting poison-animal facilities on the basis of job creation. Is a dollar worth the cost that comes with serious and sustainable health crises? Many communities know that the price is too high and have sought legal recourse in removing these facilities from their communities.

The contamination of the surrounding land, air and water has produced epidemics of physical, emotional and psychological illnesses of residents in communities near industrial poison-animal operations. Many studies have documented this enormous toxic assault. For example, a study conducted at Iowa State University confirmed that, at least, 95 percent of the dust particles drifting from CAFOs are small enough to cause respiratory problems. These small invisible particles consist of animal dander, feed, manure, molds, saliva, and bug parts. They also harbor odor and carry dangerous compounds and viruses.

The Mississippi State Department of Health (MSDH) released a review of scientific studies that detailed the health impact of residents living in communities near industrial poison-animal operations. The review confirmed: a) incidences of hydrogen sulfide and ammonia poisoning and their affects on the mental performance and mood of residents; b) the presence of elevated levels of Salmonella and antibiotic-resistant bacteria; c) the presence of oocysts of the protozoan parasite, *Cryptosporidium*; and, d) the presence of high levels of nitrates from poison-animal sewage lagoons.

PROTESTING INDUSTRIAL POISON-ANIMAL OPERATIONS

Iowa is one of the primary states that have become havens for poison-animal factories. Protests against this industry span far and wide.

The report also validated the presence of and potential for the spread of pathogens, such as *hepatitis E*, *influenza* and bacteria carrying genes for antibiotic resistance. Other studies identified a compound in poison-animal waste that has been linked to gastric ulcers and stomach cancer.[20]

Another Iowa study evaluated the health of 18 residents living within a two-mile radius of a 4,000-head poison-animal facility.[22] The residents reported problems similar to those of workers in poison-animal facilities. Some of the most common symptoms included bronchitis and hyperactive airways that featured coughing, shortness of breath, wheezing, and chest tightness. Other symptoms included nausea, weakness, dizziness, and fainting.

A study at Duke University Department of Psychiatry found significantly higher levels of tension, depression, anger, and fatigue among North Carolina residents living near large poison-animal farms when compared to rural residents located farther away from these facilities.[23]

This evidence sheds light on the notion that poison-animal meat entering the marketplace is pathogen-free. How can poison-animal meat earmarked for human consumption not contain pathogens when the excreta coming from the bodies of these animals are filled with pathogens galore?

This validates the following words by the Honorable Elijah Muhammad:

> The pig is a mass of worms. Each mouthful you eat is not a nutritious food but a mass of worms that the naked eye cannot detect. Worms thrive in the hog.

THE POISON-ANIMAL EATER, TOO

It should come as no surprise that smelling something foul can, and usually does, cause physical sickness. Each of our senses – seeing, smelling, tasting, hearing and touching – is the means of our interaction with the environment. The stimulants coming through these senses can lead to good health or sickness. We have all experienced getting sick from smelling something foul or toxic.

People who do not live near industrial poison-animal facilities are not free of the detriments caused by handling this highly toxic beast. However, contrary to what is heaped on communities near industrial poison-animal facilities, most of what poison-animal eaters' in non-farming areas suffer is self-inflicted. This is done through the preparation and consumption of poison-animal meat for breakfast, lunch and dinner.

The Honorable Elijah Muhammad writes:

> The flesh of the swine, while cooking, has a very different smell from that of other animal's flesh while cooking...In many cases, the eater of the flesh becomes nauseated when this flesh is being fried in the early morning.

These words point to the toxic effects caused by smelling poison-animal. What other type of meat emits this kind of odor? If this smell were in our drinking water or anywhere else other than in the sausage or bacon that many people, unfortunately, look forward to eating, most of us would not drink or touch it.

Cooking this poisonous beast is similar to cooking highly potent and toxic chemicals. Bacon, sausage, ham, chitterlings and spam produce the foulest of odors yet many people can withstand this stench long enough to devour this poisonous, worm-infested meat. Clearly, the smell of poison-animal should be a warning that this meat is unfit for human consumption, as well as unfit to be in our homes.

Given this fact, poison-animal eaters must seriously contemplate whether they have loss their common sense when it comes to heeding the senses that warn us of things that should not be taken into our bodies. No doubt, these senses are further destroyed by the pathogens in this poisonous flesh, which makes it easier for people to continue eating this beast. Eating this flesh takes the eater further and further into the pit of disease and dishonor.

RACIST PRACTICES

Revisiting environmental racism, reports have long confirmed that a disproportionate number of poison-animal factories are located in areas with predominant Black populations.[7] The extent of this injustice is epitomized in a study conducted in North Carolina.[24]

This study investigated:

> ...the potential that flood events can lead to environmental dispersion of animal wastes containing numerous biologic and chemical hazards in eastern North Carolina.

Hundreds of industrial poison-animal facilities operate in this state. The study was prompted by the fact that eastern North Carolina is a low-lying area, which makes it prone to flooding. This means that underground fecal waste pits also flood. In addition, fields saturated with poison-animal excreta have massive runoffs during flooding.

The investigators assessed the geographic coordinates of 2,287 poison-animal farming facilities with flood zone estimates. The estimates were derived from digital satellite images, which were taken a week after Hurricane Floyd, in 1999, brought 20 inches of rain to that area. The objective of this comparison was to determine the number of industrial poison-animal facilities operating in this flood zone.

The results showed that 237 poison-animal operations had geographic coordinates within the satellite-based flood area. The North Carolina Division of Water Quality confirmed that 46 operations had breached or flooded fecal waste pits in the same area. Of course, other facilities probably had breaches were unreported.

CAFO FLOODING

This shows dead poison-animal carcasses after a major flooding, which pollutes the waterway. The sprayfields also runoff into well-water, putting nearby residents at risk of contracting disease.

According to 2000 census data, the CAFOs within the satellite-based flood area are located in 132 census block groups, with a population of 171,498 residents. The data confirmed large populations of Black people living in these flood zones. They were significantly impacted by poison-animal excreta runoffs. Consistent with other studies, these were also areas of high poverty rates, with residents having a dependency on well-water, which is extremely susceptible to contamination during flood events.

The investigators' analysis suggested that these kinds of floods have:

> significant potential to degrade environmental health because of dispersion of wastes from industrial animal operations in areas with vulnerable populations.

Returning to the research paper, *Environmental Injustice and the Mississippi Hog Industry*, the researchers examined the location and attributes of 67 industrial poison-animal operations to determine if these operations were predominant in majority Black and poor communities.[10] The results confirmed a high prevalence of poison-animal operations in these areas. These communities had 2.4 to 3.6 times more industrial operations compared with predominantly Caucasian and affluent populations.

Another study analyzed the location and characteristics of 2,514 intensive poison-animal operations in relation to racial, economic, and water source characteristics. A sampling from localities having an average of approximately 500 households were assessed.[16] The study revealed that there were 18.9 times as many poison-animal operations in the highest quintile of poverty, as compared to the lowest. After adjustments for population density, this percentage was reduced to 7.2 times the lowest quintile. Both numbers, however, confirm a gross injustice against the poor. The study confirmed that:

- Poison-animal operations are approximately five times as common in the highest three quintiles of the percentage non-white population as compared to the lowest.
- The excess of poison-animal operations is greatest in areas with both high poverty and high percentage non-whites.
- Poison-animal corporate operations are more concentrated in poor and nonwhite areas than are operations run by independent growers.

- Most poison-animal operations, which use waste pits that contaminate groundwater, are located in areas with high dependence on well-water for drinking.

The researchers concluded that the disproportionate affects of intensive poison-animal production on:

...people of color and on the poor impede improvements in economic and environmental conditions that are needed to address public health in areas, which have high disease rates and low access to medical care as compared to other areas of the state.

On this note, morbidity and mortality from infectious diseases such as *influenza, Y. enterocolitica,* and *Salmonella* in areas that operate industrial poison-animal facilities are significantly higher in Black populations than in Caucasian populations.[25]

A FIGHT FOR LIFE

Too few so-called advocates of Black America's health issues bring up the subject of poison-animal consumption. Too few clergy and social advocates condemn the raising and consumption of poison-animal. This is probably because many of these people eat this divinely prohibited flesh.

The Honorable Elijah Muhammad fiercely condemns this meat and those who sell it. He writes:

The so-called Negroes should ban this meat from their communities and all those who sell and eat it!

REFERENCES

1. Chapin A, Boulind C, Moore A. Controlling Odor and Gaseous Emission Problems from Industrial Swine Facilities. The Kerr Center for Sustainable Agriculture Yale Environmental Protection Clinic, 1998;1-81.
2. Aillery M, Gollehon N, Johansson R, Kaplan J, Key N, Ribaudo M. Managing Manure to Improve Air and Water Quality. USDA, ERS, 2005.

3. Service ER. Confined Animal and Manure Data System. USDA, 2005.

4. North Carolina's Largest Hog Producers. Environmental Defense, 2002.

5. Hudson K. Testimony of Karen Hudson: Peoria County Board of Public Health. A Grace Factory Farm Project Report. New York, NY: Grace Resource Action Center for the Environment, 2001;1-11.

6. Meadows R. Livestock legacy. Environ Health Perspect 1995;103:1096-1100.

7. Rubin CS. Report to the State of Iowa Department of Public Health on the Investigation of the Chemical and Microbial Constituents of Ground and Surface Water Proximal to Large-Scale Swine Operations. Atlanta, GA: CDC, 1998.

8. Defense E. Raising Hogs Right: Finding Solutions in North Carolina. 1999.

9. EPA. National Emission Inventory-Ammonia Emissions from Animal Husbandry Operations. 2004.

10. Barker J. Lagoon Design and Management for Livestock Waste Treatment and Storage. Raleigh, NC: North Carolina Cooperative Extension Service, North Carolina State University, 1996.

11. Wilson S, Howell F, Wing S, Sobsey M. Environmental Injustice and the Mississippi Hog Industry. Environ Health Perspect 2002;110(Suppl 2):195-201.

12. Taraba J, Piercy L. Safe Use of Animal Waste Management Systems. Cooperative Extension Service. Department of Agricultural Engineering: University of Kentucky, College of Agriculture.

13. Mandavia S. Toxicity, Hydrogen Sulfide. Vol. 2005 eMedicine, 2001;1-5.

14. Wing S, Wolf S. Intensive Livestock Operations, Health, and Quality of Life Among Eastern North Carolina Residents. Environmental Health Perspectives 2000;108(3):233.

15. Fund ED. Atmospheric Nitrogen Deposition from Agricultural Activities. 1997.

16. Krider J. Assessing animal waste systems impacts on groundwater: occurences and potential problems. In: D'ltri F, Wolfson L, eds. Rural Groundwater Contamination. Chelsea, MI: Lewis Publishers, 1987;115-128.

17. Department of Epidemiology SoPH, University of North Carolina, Concerned Citizens of Tillery T, North Carolina. Environmental Injustice in North Carolina's Hog Industry. Environ Health Perspect 2000;108:225-231.

18. Donham KJ. Occupational Health Risks for Swine Producers: Inferences for Public Health Risks of People Living in the Vicinity of Swine Production Units. Manure Management In Harmony With the Environment and Society, 1998;299-303.

19. Brenner K, Scarpino P, Clark C. Animal viruses, coliphages, and bacteria in aerosols and wastewater at a spray irrigation site. Appl Environ Microbiol 1988(54):409-415.

20. Ribaudo M, al e. Manure Management for Water Quality: Costs to Animal Feeding Operations of Applying Nutrients to Land. USDA, ERS, 2003.

21. Cole D, Todd L, Wing S. Concentrated Swine Feeding Operations and Public Health: A Review of Occupational and Community Health Effects. Environ Health Perspect 2000;108(8):685-699

22. Thu K, al e. Proceedings from an Interdisciplinary Scientific Workshop. Impacts of Large Scale Swine Production. DesMoines, IA, 1995;17.

23. Thu K, al e. A Control Study of the Physical and Mental Health of Residents Living Near a Large-Scale Swine Operation. Journal of Agricultural Safety and Health 1997;3(1):13-26.

24. Schiffman S, al e. The Effect of Environmental Odors Emanating From Commercial Swine Operations on the Mood of Nearby Residents. Brain Research Bulletin 1995;37(4):369-375.

25. Wing S, Freedman S, Band L. The Potential Impact of Flooding on Confined Animal Feeding Operations in Eastern North Carolina. Environ Health Perspect 2002;110:387-391.

CANNOT WALK UP TO THE STORE

Poison-Animal and Rheumatic Diseases

Key Terms: angiogenesis, arthritis, asymptomatic, autoimmune diseases, fibromyalgia, hypoxia, innate immunity, lesions, lupus erythematosus, macrophages, nurse-cell, osteoarthritis, parasites, pathogenic infections, Problem 2, rheumatic diseases, rheumatism, rheumatoid arthritis, scleroderma, septic arthritis, synovial fluid, The Problem Book

* *

*T*he *Problem Book* of *The Supreme Wisdom* teaches us a thorough knowledge of the miserable condition of Black America, a people morally, mentally and spiritually destroyed through the system of slavery. In several *Problems*, we learn of the ailments identified by Master Fard Muhammad, the Great Mahdi — a Man who came from the Circle of the Wise Scientists or Elders, as described in the Bible, in the Book of Revelations. According to what HE taught the Honorable Elijah Muhammad, these Men live hundreds of years. We should expect Men of such divine power to live longer than the average life spans of people of *this world*.

Anyone who knows how to live hundreds of years also knows the kind of living that diminishes one's lifespan to tens of years — 40, 50 and 60. Such a Master of the life force is able to identify, very quickly, why we suffer the ailments we suffer. Therefore, we should expect Master Fard Muhammad to have the deepest knowledge of the root of our health problems. He demonstrated this when HE came among us, and left *The Problem Book* with the Honorable Elijah Muhammad that each of us may participate in solving our own problems.

In *Problem 2*, Master Fard Muhammad states:

> The wife of Mr. W. D. Fard's uncle, in the wilderness of North America, weighs other than herself, therefore, she has rheumatism, headaches, pain in all joints, and cannot walk up to the store. She is troubled frequently with high blood pressure and registers more than thirty-two. Her pulse is nearly eighty times per minute and she died at the age of forty-seven. How many times did her pulse beat in forty-seven years?

The Black man and woman of America represent the uncle and aunt, respectively, of Master Fard Muhammad. These terms have great meaning. Generally, they confirm the Black man and woman's connection to the Family of the Creator, and show our importance to the Divine Elders mentioned in the Book of Revelations.

In analyzing *Problem 2*, we can relate the health bouts experienced by the Black woman of America, the wife of Mr. W. D. Fard's uncle, to the pathologies of pathogenic infections. Most of us are all too familiar with these health conditions. Rheumatism, arthritis (joint pain), headaches and high blood pressure are common afflictions in Black America.

Most, if not all, of us know someone suffering from these afflictions. We also know of persons who have died at 47 to 50 years of age because of these ailments. This shows that we begin battling diseases after a few decades of life. This, too, we also know to be 100 percent true.

RHEUMATISM OR RHEUMATIC DISEASES

. . . .

A multitude of medical terms describe and define the many health ailments that represent the perils of eating poison-animal. A few of these diseases were described in Chapter 6 and attest to the enormity of the destruction occurring in the human vessel caused by the infestation of pathogens.

Rheumatism refers to *rheumatic diseases*. The National Institute of Arthritis and Musculoskeletal and Skin Diseases (NIAMS) describes rheumatic diseases:[1]

> Rheumatic diseases are characterized by inflammation (signs are redness and/or heat, swelling, and pain) and loss of function of one or more connecting or supporting structures of the body. They especially affect joints, tendons, ligaments, bones, and muscles. Common symptoms are pain, swelling, and stiffness. Some rheumatic diseases can also involve internal organs. There are more than 100 rheumatic diseases.

Several rheumatic diseases include osteoarthritis, rheumatoid arthritis, lupus erythematosus, juvenile rheumatoid arthritis, gout, fibromyalgia, bursitis, rheumatic fever, and Lyme disease. As indicated, the word "arthritis" is also included. Arthritis means joint inflammation. The "pain in all joints" stated in *Problem 2* could easily refer to arthritis.

Rheumatic diseases are basically diseases that involve the immune system, and are classified according to specific immunological pathologies; hence, the broad scope of diseases within this classification. Some of these diseases involve connective tissues, such as tendons, which support the framework of the body and its internal organs. These diseases are among the worst type because they often lead to organ failures and death.

Other types of diseases involve joint areas. An underlying feature of rheumatic diseases is the continuous release of immunological substances that produce constant inflammation, as well as destroy valuable tissue and fluids in the muscles and joints. This underlying working is classified as autoimmune disease, which results from immune reactions that act on the good tissues as well as the foreign substances in the body. This concept, however, is controversial.

The intelligent workings of the parasites show that they cause diseases of both the tendons and joints, as they infest the muscles and disrupt the immune system. Viruses, fungi and bacteria, on the other hand, severely disturb the immune system causing inflammation to occur in muscles, tendons, and joints. Fungi and bacteria are also known to lodge in joint areas. Overall, these pathogens cause one or more rheumatic diseases.

A poison-animal eater will experience the most severe tissue, muscle and joint problems and pain because the poison-animal is a repository for 999 germs. These germs – parasites, fungi, viruses, and bacteria – overrun the person's body, as they scrounge the victim's life away.

BACK, CUTANEOUS NERVES, POSTERIOR VIEW

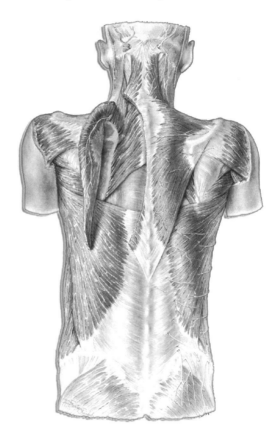

Parasites infest the tissues of the body causing disruptions to immune processes that lead to inflammatory conditions.

In addition, the mutilation of the intestinal lining opens the door for a litany of other pathogens that jump at the opportunity to take up residence in the poison-animal eater's body. An all out invasion of the body is taking place. Such a massive incursion continues until death comes to put an end to it. Of course, after death, other pathogens come on the scene to complete the mutilation.

The pain associated with the mass infestation of pathogens in the body is a way of telling the person that something terrible is happening to them. It is this excruciating pain that prevents the wife of Mr. W. D. Fard's uncle from being able to *walk up to the store* to obtain the necessities to support her family. This physical restriction generally means that her ability to effectively serve as mother, nurse, and wife, as well as her ability to care for herself, is severely diminished.

In her husband's case, Mr. W. D. Fard's uncle, the afflictions of rheumatism means that his ability to provide for his family and display leadership within his family and community are hampered. This is the principle effect of rheumatic diseases — the gradual incapacitation of the person, in an extraordinarily painful way.

There is no way that anyone can be convinced that the Creator intended humans to suffer like this. The mere thought that these sorts of afflictions begin within three to four decades of life proves that this world's way of life is contrary to what Almighty God intends for humans.

THE BURDEN OF RHEUMATISM

According to the Center for Disease Control and Prevention, rheumatic diseases are among the most prevalent chronic diseases in the United States (U.S.), and a leading cause of disability.[2] Health researchers estimate that nearly 43 million Americans are afflicted with rheumatic disease.[3] Within this group, approximately 21 million are estimated to have osteoarthritis; an estimated four million have fibromyalgia; and, two million have rheumatoid arthritis.[4] These estimates are on the low end.

With respect to gender, women are more afflicted with rheumatic diseases than are men. For example, lupus, rheumatoid arthritis, scleroderma, and fibromyalgia are more common among women.[4] Rheumatoid arthritis occurs two to three times more often in women than in men. Researchers suggest that this indicates that hormones and other male-female biological differences have roles in the development of these conditions.

Race has also been a noted factor in the prevalence of rheumatic diseases. As with other major chronic conditions, Black America is extremely burdened with this class of disease, as well. The following is stated in the article, *Racial/Ethnic Difference in the Prevalence and Impact of Doctor-Diagnosed Arthritis – United States, 2002*, which appeared in an issue of Morbidity & Mortality Weekly Report:

> This report summarizes the results of that analysis, which indicate that, when compared with whites, a higher proportion of blacks had arthritis-attributable activity limitations, work limitations, and severe joint pain, and a higher proportion of Hispanics had arthritis-attributable work limitations and severe joint pain.

The report notes that the type of work performed – primarily manual labor – is a leading contributor to these conditions; however, this is far from the reality of the root cause of these conditions. Our limbs are made for use. In fact, sedentary lifestyles contribute to physical degeneration through the atrophy of underutilized muscles. The primary cause of this condition is diet-related, as identified by Master Fard Muhammad. This report makes no mention of diet as a possible cause.

Reflecting the same disease prevalence as the overall population, Black women are more afflicted with rheumatic diseases than are Black men. Among the diseases that wreck havoc, lupus erythematosus heavily afflicts Black women. Its occurrence is three times more common in Black women than in Caucasian women.[1]

PATHOGENIC LINK TO RHEUMATIC DISEASES

As with other pathogen-related afflictions, we can safely assume that few people suffering from arthritic conditions have connected their health plight to parasitic or pathogenic infections. What person wants to think that they are infested with parasites? People are not inclined to think this; albeit, many rheumatic diseases result from extreme disturbances by pathogens. This means that there is a greater likelihood that these health afflictions are the result of pathogenic infestations; however, few people are aware of this.

SHOULDER JOINT, ANTEROLATERAL VIEW

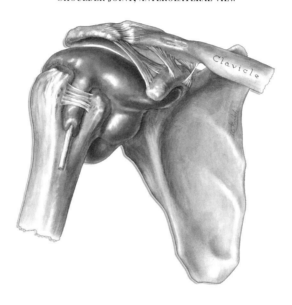

Parasites elicit immune responses that destroy the fluid and tissues that support the joints. Some pathogens also lodge in joint areas.

PATHOGEN-GENERATED AUTOIMMUNE DISEASES

Pathogens have long proved to be leading causes of autoimmune diseases. Let us consider lupus erythematosus, which severely afflicts Black women. This condition is regarded as an autoimmune disease, which again, causes the immune system to release substances to combat invaders. This causes inflammation of and damage to the joints, skin, kidneys, heart, lungs, blood vessels, and brain.

Although this world's bogus healthcare system wants many women to believe that the cause of this condition is unknown, lupus erythematosus is heavily linked, directly and indirectly, to infestation by parasites, bacteria, viruses and fungi.[5] Some health experts have postulated that drugs, smoking and environmental pollutants are triggers for the disease.[6] This has some merit.

The workings of autoimmune diseases provide insight into the connection of rheumatic diseases to pathogens. Let us consider the term autoimmune disease. On face value, the term implies that the immune system is acting out of sorts — that there are no invaders so the healthy tissues become the target. This term also makes us inclined to believe that these conditions are either genetically-driven or outside of our control — meaning that what we breath, eat, drink and think have little to do with the ailments we suffer. This is far from the truth. Such a term; therefore, can be somewhat deceptive as it suggests that this condition is the cause of the disease rather than the effect of an infection.

The pathogens' awesome ability to arrest the immune system, causing it to act and react on behalf of the pathogens, tells us much about autoimmune disease. For example, lupus erythematosus is characterized by a complex interplay among overactive B cells, abnormally activated T cells, and antigen-presenting cells.[7] This represents an overproduction of an array of inflammatory substances, which is evidence that something foreign has infected the body.

Scientists may not be able to pinpoint the exact origin of the disturbance, but they have a large pool of pathogens and pollutants from which to choose. Considering that people eat pounds of poison-animal makes it highly probable that pathogens from this diseased meat are a cause of these health ailments.

The foremost problem is that there is no consensus among the medical community to ban poison-animal from the human food chain. The Honorable Elijah Muhammad is correct when He states that doctors know the health damage caused by eating poison-animal, but do not tell their patients to stop eating it, for fear they may lose profits.

The research article, *Role for Innate Immunity in Rheumatoid Arthritis,* resurfaced the issue of "innate immunity", in association with its importance to autoimmune and inflammatory diseases:[8]

> After a long period of neglect, innate immunity is again recognized as a key mechanism not only in preventing invasion of the body by microorganisms, but also in contributing to the pathogenesis of autoimmune and inflammatory diseases by deviating the immune response or promoting the emergence of a regulatory response.

Innate immunity is considered the first line of defense. The immune system is triggered when it recognizes foreign substances or if it is taken hostage by highly intelligent pathogens. The immune system does not go berserk without reason. Something sends it into disarray.

The immune system does not only respond to invading pathogens, but also reacts when tissue is damaged. Most of us have experienced some type of laceration or bruise where the tissue is clearly damaged. Swelling ensues, which is the primary response. This indicates that the immune system is going about its work of healing and preventing infections.

In Chapter 5, we discussed the Trichinella parasite's work in causing lesions in the muscle tissues. This enables the parasite to secure the substances required for long-term survival in its nurse-cell. The formation of the nurse-cell, along with continued processes to sustain the cell, inflicts damage on the muscle tissues by causing hypoxia to occur.

As previously described, hypoxia is a deficiency in the amount of oxygen in tissues. A tissue starved of oxygen begins to degenerate, and consequently, triggers the wound healing process, *angiogenesis*. This systematic process keeps the immune system activated for the good of the parasite.

Wound healing is a phenomenal process. What does it take to heal damaged tissue? What substances must the immune system dispatch to begin a process that both protects and heals the injured tissues? When considering these questions, we get a sense of why swelling or inflammation occurs and usually remains for several days. This is the case with the swelling of outer layers of the skin, as well as internal tissues and organs. Inflammation is a natural part of the immune response and healing process.

Unfortunately, most people do not view arthritis and other rheumatic diseases as responses to injuries, which trigger inflammation. What are these injuries? Microscopic images of parasites and other pathogens reveal anatomical structures that resemble teeth. This is how pathogens burrow into the flesh. Therefore, the poison-animal eater is continuously being bitten – literally to death – from scores of pathogens.

ANCYLOSTOMA DUODENALE HOOKWORM

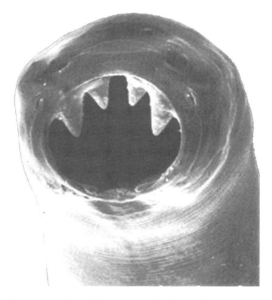

The presence of four cutting "teeth," two on each side, enables the parasite to burrow in the person's intestinal lining or muscle tissues.
Courtesy of Graphic Images of Parasites
(http://www.biosci.ohio-state.edu/~parasite/hookworm_adults.html)

If we had this view of pathogenic infections, there would be greater effort to get to the root of our diseases and ailments. However, not realizing or considering this makes us susceptible to following recommendations to take medications that do not rid our bodies of pathogens — live or chemical.

The latter weighs heavily on diet, specifically how often we eat food. According to the Honorable Elijah Muhammad and the scientific research that supports His words, eating food too often overwhelms our bodies with natural and unnatural toxins, not to mention the pathogens already discussed. These poisons trigger allergic reactions that manifest as chronic arthritic conditions.

In the study of various rheumatic diseases, the affect of hypoxia has been well noted. The research study, *Hypoxia Regulates Macrophage Functions in Inflammation*, describes the involvement of hypoxia with rheumatic conditions:[9]

> Hypoxia is a prominent feature of various inflamed, diseased tissues, including malignant tumors, atherosclerotic plaques, myocardial infarcts, the synovia of joints with rheumatoid arthritis, healing wounds, and sites of bacterial infection.

The study's researchers described how macrophages have a role in both defending and healing damaged tissues; and their contribution to arthritic conditions by accumulating in ischemic or hypoxic sites. Macrophages are cells found in tissues and are responsible for engulfing and ingesting (phagocytosis) pathogens, dead cells and cellular debris. These phagocytic cells are part of the innate immune system and are unleashed when tissue damage occurs.

Ischemic means a decrease in the blood supply to tissue caused by constriction or obstruction of blood vessels. The fact that some pathogens travel throughout the body in blood vessels confirms their involvement in causing ischemic conditions.

HISTORICAL LINK

The connection between rheumatoid arthritis and "infectious agents" has been noted since the early 1900s.[10] This connection is now resurfacing and making its way into scientific literature. A very insightful article, having a title that begs the question, *Is There a Role for Parasites in the Etiology of Inflammatory Rheumatism?*, describes parasitic rheumatism as being characterized by inflammatory joint manifestations caused by circulating immunological substances in both serum and synovial fluid; and by immunoglobulins and complement deposits in synovium.[11]

Synovial fluid is a clear, viscid lubricating fluid secreted by membranes in joint cavities, sheaths of tendons, and bursae — sac-like bodily cavities, especially containing viscous lubricating fluids located between a tendon and a bone or at points of friction between moving structures. This fluid gets contaminated with immunologic substances causing it to harden; or at worst, causing its destruction.

This article, written in 1990, also noted the increase in the number of parasites that cause rheumatic disease:

> The number of parasites (now 15) which can induce such an arthritis by immune mechanisms is steadily increasing. In all but a few cases of parasitic rheumatism, usual parasitic manifestations (diarrhea, abdominal pain, nausea...) are mild or absent; but, if present, they are a very good criteria to evoke the diagnosis.

The researchers described the clinical picture of arthritis induced by parasitic infestation as being: 1) very polymorphic — occurring in different forms, stages, or types; 2) nonspecific of the involved parasite; and, 3) causing symptoms that are monoarticular (affecting one joint), pauciarticular (affecting four or fewer joints), or polyarticular (affecting many joints).

These manifestations also mimic the clinical outlook of different inflammatory diseases, which means that unless the person is diagnosed with the parasitic infection, he or she will continue with the parasite-induced rheumatic disease because the parasites will remain in the person's body.

Most often, antirheumatic drugs fail to treat parasite-induced rheumatism,[12] which is an obvious indicator that parasites might be at the root of the condition. How many doctors will consider this? Will they recommend other drugs instead of testing for parasitic infections? There is a higher probability that they will continue with other drug therapies, to no avail. People will watch their conditions worsen, as is the norm in this world — few are ever healed of anything.

The connection between bacteria and viruses to rheumatic disease has also been the subject of recent studies. In a landmark study, the clinical features of 150 patients were assessed to determine the pathogens responsible for the septic arthritis that burdened all patients.[13] Septic arthritis is caused by sepsis, which is the presence of pathogenic organisms or their toxins in the blood or tissues.

ANTERIOR ASPECTS OF WRIST AND HAND

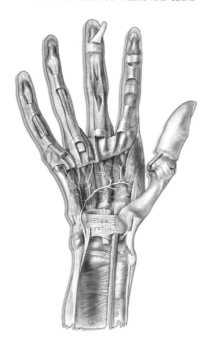

Inflammatory diseases, such as arthritis, gout, and scleroderma wreck havoc on the body's extremities such as the hands and feet.

The study involved patients in two community hospitals in northern Israel. The researchers assessed cases covering a 17-year period, between 1987 and 2003. Of the 150 cases, 110 patients met the criteria for the case definition of septic arthritis. The average age of the patients was 37 years. The assessment determined that primary joint disease was reported in approximately 22 percent of the cases, with osteoarthritis being most prevalent (8.1%).

With respect to the pathogens that caused the septic arthritis, *Staphylococcus aureus* was the most common, making up 40 percent of all positive cultures. This pathogen is the source of Staphylococcal food-poisoning, and symptoms include nausea, vomiting, retching, abdominal cramping, and prostration. In more severe cases, headache, muscle cramping, and transient changes in blood pressure and pulse rate occur. This pathogen is prevalent in poison-animal.[14]

In another study, researchers identified "reactive arthritis" as a "classical" result of infection from enteric pathogens such as Yersinia, Salmonella, Campylobacter and Shigella bacteria.[15] Additionally, inflammatory arthritis has been described in enteric infections caused by organisms such as Clostridium difficile, Brucella and Giardia. The pathogen Tropheryma whippelii (Whipple's disease) was also identified as a causal agent for arthritis. These pathogens are also harbored in poison-animal.[16]

We must reiterate that a multitude of parasites, bacterium, viruses, or fungi flourish in poison-animal. This is an animal genetically-manufactured to absorb poisons of all kinds.

NO GOOD OUTLOOK

Unfortunately, the outlook for rheumatic disease is very gloomy. Despite the current high prevalence, the incidence is expected to increase in the United States population. The CDC estimates that by the year 2020, an estimated 60 million people will have some type of arthritic disease.[17] Additionally, nearly 12 million people are forecasted to be afflicted with arthritis-related disability. Of course, these numbers are on the low end.

Although epidemiologists point to an aging population as the reason for this astronomical rise, the increase in industrial poison-animal farming, producing the increased marketing of this meat, is a significant contributor to this rise. The process of aging is directly related to degeneration, which can result from parasitic infestations, as well.

SUCCESSFULLY ROBBED

The pandemic of rheumatic disease caused by poison-animal pathogens is another form of robbery of both wealth and life of the poison-animal eater. The CDC estimates that the cost associated with these diseases is $65 billion per year. This figure includes $15 billion for medical expenses, which comprises expenses for 39 million physician visits and more than one-half million hospitalizations.[18] The remaining $50 billion is assigned to lost wages from absences and long-term leaves from employment and poor work performance.

Who foots this bill? Taxpayers and those inflicted with this disease are the primary payers. The changing scope of the medical insurance landscape means that most people will gradually pay out-of-pocket for their medical expenses. In addition, the costs of medication is rising by leaps and bounds.

Making matters worse is that the *merchants of disease and death* continue with the deception of not revealing to the public that poison-animal is a principle avenue of pathogens that cause rheumatic diseases.

REFERENCES

1. NIAMA. Questions & Answers About Arthritis and Rheumatic Diseases. Bethesda: NIH, DHHS, 2004;40.
2. CDC. Prevalence of disabilities and associated health conditions - United States. MMWR 1994;43(40):730-39.
3. CDC. Prevalence and impact of chronic joint symptoms - seven states. MMWR 1996;47(17):345-51.
4. Lawrence R, Helmick C, Arnett F. Estimates of the prevalence of arthritis and selected musculoskeletal disorders in the United States. Arthritis Rheum 1998;41:778-99.
5. Kasapcopur O, Ergul Y, Kutlug S, Candan C, Camcioglu Y, Arisoy N. Systemic lupus erythematosus due to Epstein-Barr virus or Epstein-Barr virus infection

provocating acute exacerbation of systemic lupus erythematosus? Rheumatol Int 2005(1-3).

6. Sarzi-Puttini P, Atzeni F, Iaccarino L, Doria A. Environment and systemic lupus erythematosus: an overview. Autoimmunity 2005;38(7):465-72.

7. Kyttaris V, Katsiari C, Juang Y, Tsokos G. New insights into the pathogenesis of systemic lupus erythematosus. Curr Rheumatol Rep 2005;7(6):469-75.

8. Falgarone G, Jaen O, Boisser M. Role for innate immunity in rheumatoid arthritis. Joint Bone Spine 2005;72(1):17-25.

9. Murdoch C, Muthana M, Lewis C. Hypoxia regulates macrophage functions in inflammation. J Immunol. 2005 Nov 15;175(10):6257-63. 2005;175(10):6257-63.

10. Torrey E, Yolken R. The Schizophrenia–Rheumatoid Arthritis Connection: Infectious, Immune, or Both? Brain Behav Immun 2001;15(4):401-410.

11. Doury P. [Is there a role for parasites in the etiology of inflammatory rheumatism?] [Article in French]. Bull Acad Natl Med 1990;174(6):743-51; discussion 751-4.

12. McGill P. Rheumatic syndromes associated with parasites. Baillieres Clin Rheumatol 1995;9(1):201-13.

13. Eder L, Zisman D, Rozenbaum M, Rosner I. Clinical features and aetiology of septic arthritis in northern Israel. Rheumatology (Oxford) 2005;Sept 7.

14. Lee JH. Methicillin (Oxacillin)-Resistant Staphylococcus aureus Strains Isolated from Major Food Animals and Their Potential Transmission to Humans. Appl. Environ. Microbiol. 2003;69(11):6489-6494.

15. Hill Gaston J, Lillicrap M. Arthritis associated with enteric infection. Best Pract Res Clin Rheumatol 2003;17(2):219-39.

16. Thurston-Enriquez J, Gilley J, Eghball B. Microbial quality of runoff following land application of cattle manure and swine slurry. J Water Health 2005;3(2):157-71.

17. CDC. Arthritis prevalence and activity limitations - United States. MMWR 1994;43(24):433-8.

18. Yelin E, Callahan L. The economic cost and social and psychological impact of musculoskeletal conditions. Arthritis Rheum 1995;38(10):1351-62.

10

MOTHER TO CHILD

Passing On Poison-Animal Pathogens

Key Terms: amniotic sac, congenital infection, congenital toxoplasmosis, congenital trichinosis, genetic predisposition, genitalia, host-to-host transmission, immune system, low-birth-weight, microorganisms, pathogens, perinatal mortality, placenta, sepsis, spontaneous abortions, transmammary infection, transplacental infection

T he Scriptures of the Bible, Exodus 20:5, reminds us of the *sins of the fathers being visited upon the children*. We are also reminded in Genesis 12:7 of the great promises Almighty God made to HIS worthy servants, which included their seed — who became the recipients or benefactors of these promises. In these references, rest the true essence of inheritance, which is not how much money, jewelry or property a person leaves to their children, but the righteousness of their living and good works. Also, the means by which the parents acquired their wealth determines whether or not their children are favored or cursed by Almighty God — the sins being visited upon the children.

Whether or not Almighty God's wrath or favor is passed to our children, this action is not confined to deliberate acts on HIS part, inasmuch as it is a law of nature — hence, the concept of genetic predisposition.

A simplistic view of this concept, *genetic predisposition*, is that our biological children are comprised of our genetic material or DNA (deoxyribonucleic acid). Therefore, our children are predisposed to whatever is in our genetic material. To some extent, our children's potential and future are written in the genes we give them, which becomes their genetic makeup.

This truth is demonstrated in the science of breeding. For example, the mating of thoroughbred race horses produces offspring that are potentially superior to their parents. The same is true for humans. By adhering to the science of mating, humans can produce children predestined to accomplish specific works.

This is the way the Creator established the order of procreation and human advancement. Each generation is supposed to achieve a greater expression of human potential than the previous generations. Each generation is supposed to demonstrate greater divine qualities.

In this world, unfortunately, the situation has been the opposite. Children are born into a world that requires them to overcome astronomical hurdles in order to develop and utilize their God-given gifts and talents. In fact, merely identifying or finding one's innate gifts is a major challenge in a world filled with millions of petty distractions. The reasons are clear.

The rulers of this world intend for everyone to serve as tools and slaves so that the ruling class can live in luxury. As a result, children have become a "marketing concept" for the *merchants of indecency and death*.

Also, the greed of the older generations has made obtaining the necessities of life an uphill road for future generations. The ever-increasing costs of houses, automobiles, and education only means that what is now a suitable income for comfortable living will put people in the rolls of the impoverished in decades to come.

Atop these unnecessary adversities are genetic predispositions to a multitude of ailments because of poor dietary habits and reckless lifestyles, on the part of many parents. Children are the victims of the selfish and ignorant acts of their parents.

PARASITE'S CONGENITAL CAPABILITIES

In the nature of every creature is the undaunted struggle to see both itself and its offspring survive. Intrinsic in this is the quest to ensure the species evolutionary permanence; therefore, many creatures labor to make conditions suitable for the survival of their offspring.

As mentioned several times throughout this book, parasites seek to secure the survival of their offspring through host-to-host transmission. We have learned that one of the ways this is achieved is through the encapsulation of larvae in the infected host's muscles. When other hosts eat this infected flesh, the parasites are transferred to them. The new host now becomes the home of the parasites. This cycle of survival continues for decades and centuries.

Another means of host-to-host transmission is from mother-to-offspring — that is, a mother infected with a pathogen or parasite transfers the larvae to her unborn child. This particular form of transmission is called *congenital infection*.

Although the concept of congenital infection might be new to the non-medical person, this subject is very prominent in the field of pediatric care. Microorganisms, including larvae, are transferred to the offspring through the mother's reproductive organs, primarily by gaining access to the mother's external genitalia, the placenta, or the birth canal.[1]

Infections occurring through the external genitalia are called *ascending infections.*[2] By infecting this area, microorganisms are able to gain access to the mother's amniotic sac. The amniotic sac is where the unborn child or fetus lives, and is the means by which the fetus acquires the nutrients it needs for further growth and development. Therefore, pathogens are in the true home of the fetus when they infest the amniotic sac.

The infestation of the amniotic sac causes the sac to degenerate, often causing it to rupture. As with other organs infested by pathogens, the immune system goes to work within the sac's tissue to fight the parasitic infection. This causes inflammation of the sac, which can trigger labor and bring about premature birth. No doubt, premature birth threatens the life of the mother and the child.

FEMALE REPRODUCTIVE AREA

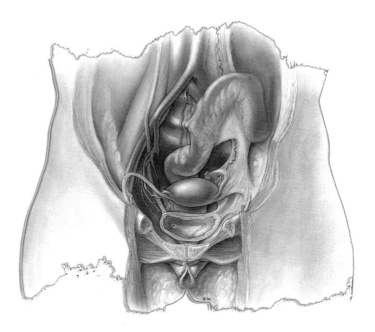

Parasites invade the reproductive area and await opportunities to infect the fetus.

The pathogenic infestation of the amniotic fluid means that nearly anything and everything that favors the pathogens' survival can be achieved, to the detriment of the unborn child. During infections, the fetus consumes the microorganisms through the nose and mouth, infecting its lungs. The pathogens may also penetrate other orifices of the fetus, such as the ear canal.

The infection of the placenta is known as *transplacental infection*. Pathogens that circulate in the mother's blood can make their way to the placenta, contaminating the fetus. The burrowing of parasites in the placenta gradually destroys it, and immunological responses cause inflammation of the organ, which often does not resolve the infection. Contrarily, these responses cause complications that degenerate the physical development of the fetus, potentially causing death. The mother may also suffer a litany of ailments.

The pathogens that cannot ascend to the amniotic sac or enter the placenta, colonize at the birth canal and await the delivery of the child. During the delivery process, the pathogens contaminate the maternal blood and related secretions, and infect the infant as it passes through the birth canal.

Infections can also occur after birth, particularly during nursing or breastfeeding. This form of infection is called *transmammary infection*. Pathogens lodge in the mammary glands and infect the mother's milk. Several parasites are known for causing transmammary infections.

For example, biochemical studies revealed the presence of *Strongyloides* larvae in breast milk, and confirmed that infants were infected with both Strongyloides fuelleborni and hookworm species through breast milk.[3] Infections by this class of parasites cause abdominal pain, vomiting and intermittent diarrhea. Dysentery and weight loss are associated with chronic infections. The parasites also migrate through the lungs inducing many immunological reactions that can cause severe respiratory problems.

Considering this, there is no doubt that congenital infections cause an array of severe health consequences to both the mother and the fetus. Spontaneous abortions and perinatal mortality are common occurrences in these types of infections — usually between conception and the 22nd week of pregnancy.

The general perspective regarding this issue is that if the infection occurs during the first 20 weeks, there is a high probability that fetal death will result. On the other hand, infections that take place between the 20th and 37th week are known to cause pre-term labor and delivery, which can result in fetal death or morbidity due to low-birth-weight.

Infections that occur during passage through the birth canal usually cause the infant to develop afflictions that lead to sepsis, potentially causing death within the first days of life.

FEMALE MAMMARY GLAND

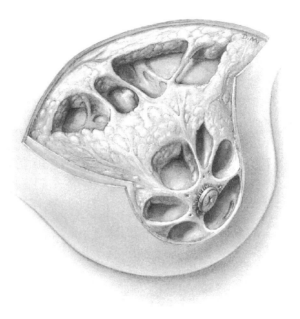

Parasites infest the mammary gland and infect the mother's milk. Infants become
infected when nursing.

The primary concern with congenital infections is that most of them
affect the brain of the fetus. Parasites and viruses possess an affinity
for the brain and nervous system. This is a very interesting
phenomenon, as it shows that internal warfare is underway — the
intelligent parasite seeks to establish a beachhead in the seat of the
host's intelligence.

When the congenital infection occurs early in the pregnancy there is
a strong likelihood that the infant's brain will be damaged.[4] This
damage includes, but is not limited to, microcephaly, brain atrophy,
hydrocephalus, neuronal migrational anomalies and cerebral
calcifications.[5] Overall, this destruction leads to permanent

developmental problems and abnormalities. The child experiences lifelong disabilities, if it survives.

Researchers have not identified all the microorganisms capable of causing congenital infections. Many parasites, viruses, bacteria and fungi are capable of infecting the female reproductive areas to infect the child. The intelligent nature of these pathogens, combined with their microscopic size, makes any of them capable of infecting the fetus. Some of the known pathogens that cause congenital infections include Treponema pallidum (Syphilis), Toxoplasma gondii and Trichinella parasites; Rubella, human parvoviruses, Varicella-zoster virus, Cytomegalovirus,6 Listeria monocytogenes, Salmonella bacteria, hepatitis viruses, Neisseria gonnorheae, human immunodeficiency virus (HIV), Herpes Simplex Virus (HSV), Mycoplasma species and Group B Streptococcus bacteria.

FEMALE PELVIS, MEDIAN SECTION

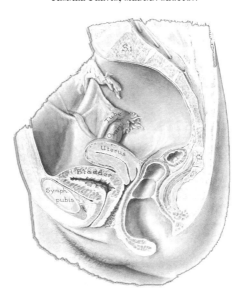

Parasites, bacteria, and viruses are capable of infecting the female reproductive areas
and are alerted when pregnancy develops. This shows their intelligent nature to secure
the survival of their offspring by transmitting their eggs to the human fetus.

CONGENITAL INFECTION-CAUSING PATHOGENS

Poison-animal harbors the pathogens listed in the previous section, which is still a far cry from the 999 germs that persist in this genetically-engineered animal. As other pathogens become known, the poison-animal becomes that much more undesirable to look upon, and especially to eat. Eventually, we will run this animal off the cliff into a lake of fire.

The workings of pathogens such as Toxoplasma gondii and Trichinella, in relation to poison-animal, have been addressed. The following sections conveys the current research associated with congenital infections caused by these specific parasites.

TRICHINELLA SPECIES

As the leading "super" parasite, we can expect Trichinella to move from mother to child during pregnancies. The ability of this parasite to infect nearly every organ in the body makes the threat of congenital trichinosis highly likely in women infested with this parasite before and during pregnancy.

A landmark case of a large outbreak of trichinosis in the Slovak Republic, demonstrated the awesome congenital capability of the Trichinella parasite.[7] The outbreak involved the Trichinella britovi species and 336 people. A woman in her 10th week of pregnancy was among those infected. She was treated with mebendazole, an anthelminthic drug.

The infected woman ultimately decided to abort the pregnancy at the 22nd week. An immunocytochemical examination confirmed that Trichinella larvae had infested the fetus. There is no doubt that the fetus would have experienced many severe health problems, if it survived.

We must note here that controversy surrounds the use of anthelminthic drugs. These potent drugs are considered unsafe, and in some cases ineffective, in ridding the body of parasites. The drugs often cause side-effects that lead to severe complications.

If Trichinella is the *super* parasite, then what we have learned about Toxoplasma gondii (T. gondii) places it closely behind Trichinella. According to the Centers for Disease Control and Prevention (CDC) Toxoplasmosis is the third leading cause of foodborne deaths in the United States (U.S.).[8] The CDC further estimates that 225,000 cases of toxoplasmosis occur every year in the United States, resulting in 5,000 hospitalizations and 750 deaths.

Of the 750 deaths that occur each year, approximately one-half is attributed to food contamination. Poison-animal has been implicated as the meat most commonly associated with foodborne toxoplasmosis.[9] In the U.S., epidemiologists estimate that 32 percent of pork products are contaminated with T. gondii parasites.

Congenital toxoplasmosis is a major problem throughout the world, particularly because billions of people are infected with this parasite. In the U.S., an estimated 23 percent of adolescents and adults have laboratory evidence of T. gondii infection; although not everyone infected develops acute toxoplasmosis. Nevertheless, this means that nearly one-fourth of childbearing-aged women are potentially infected with this pathogen, making a congenital toxoplasmosis pandemic highly probable.

Estimates of congenital toxoplasmosis in the U.S. range from 400 to 4,000 cases each year. The margin is wide because congenital toxoplasmosis is not a nationally reportable disease and no national data is available regarding its prevalence. The high adult infection rate bears heavily on this estimation.

As with trichinosis, congenital toxoplasmosis is known to cause serious health problems in the fetus, as well as chronic conditions to the infant. The classic triad of signs suggestive of congenital toxoplasmosis includes chorioretinitis, intracranial calcifications, and hydrocephalus. Chorioretinitis is inflammation of the choroid and retina. In Chapter 7, we covered the morbidity associated with brain calcifications and hydrocephalus.

Untreated maternal toxoplasmosis infections are usually transmitted to the fetus.[10] In routine examinations, most infants infected in the uterus are born with no obvious signs of this disease, but many develop learning and visual disabilities shortly thereafter.[11] When left untreated, congenital toxoplasmosis is associated with severe disease and fatality.[12] Severe conditions include mental retardation, blindness, and epilepsy.[13]

PREVALENCE OF BIRTHING PROBLEMS

Obviously, congenital infections of poison-animal pathogens make the female poison-animal eater a risk factor to her unborn child. Considering the high consumption of poison-animal within Black America (63 pounds annually) in light of the high incidences of fetal death, low-birth-weights, very-low-birth-weights, infant death syndrome, and childhood mental developmental disorders, reveal a probable epidemic of congenital infections in Black America. Few health researchers mention this issue when addressing Black America's health problems. Why is this?

Again, there has never been a sincere effort from those who govern the U.S. to address the healthcare needs of Black America. This noble and humane goal would lead to a reduction in earnings for the major profit centers that uphold the economic foundation of this nation — the food and healthcare industries.

Black health professional and advocates, too, fall short in condemning the eating of poison-animal because many of them eat this divinely-forbidden and despicable meat. In addition, nearly all of them look for this world's institutions to guide their steps. This, of course, makes them inept.

There is no doubt that congenital parasitic infections span America. The U.S. infant mortality rate is higher than that of 27 other nations.[14] This sheds light on the fact that so-called "developed" nations have health plights equal to or worse than those of so-called developing or "Third World" countries, although scientists living in industrialized countries want people to believe otherwise. Notwithstanding, the evidence reveals that developed nations are beset with a multitude of parasitic infections, and have no more control over the spread of these pathogens than do those living in a tiny village in Zimbabwe.

According to the CDC, in the year 2000, nearly 28,000 infants died before their first birthday — a rate of approximately 7 deaths per 1,000 live births. Also in 2000, the infant mortality rate per 1000 live births for babies born to Black people of America was nearly 14, which was and remains twice the national rate. In comparison, the infant mortality rates were 8.2 for Native Americans, 5.6 for Hispanics and 5.7 for Caucasians.

Unfortunately, the high incidence of infant diseases and mortality in Black America is not a new experience. Again, our disastrous health plight is rooted in the era of slavery. Our miserable condition proves that we have not shaken the scourges of slavery. We continue to eat poison-animal and other unhealthy foods that give pathogens an opportunity to destroy our future.

The onslaught of fetal death, infant mortality, and drastic childhood behavioral and mental problems afflicting Black America should inspire us to make an all-out effort to banish poison-animal from our diets. We cannot disobey divine law, consequently experiencing health atrocities, and then expect an uncompassionate social system to come to our rescue. This is not intelligence. Obedience to divine law has built-in protective factors that ensure success.

REFERENCES

1. Pereira L, Maidji E, McDonagh S, Tabata T. Insights into viral transmission at the uterine-placental interface. Trends Microbiol. 2005;13(4):164-74.
2. Glukhovets N, Fadeev A. The importance of specialised pathology service in diagnosis of ascending infection of the reproductive system in pregnant women. Arkh Patol [Article in Russian] 2005;67(1):46-9
3. Brown R, Girardeau H. Transmammary passage of Strongyloides sp. larvae in the human host. Am J Trop Med Hyg 1977;26(2):215-9.
4. Becker L. Infections of the developing brain. AJNR 1992;13:537-549.
5. Osborn R, Byrd S. Congenital infections of the brain. Neuroimag. Clin. N. Amer 1991;1(1):105-118.
6. Pereira L, Maidji E, McDonagh S, Tabata T. Insights into viral transmission at the uterine-placental interface. Trends Microbiol. 2005;13(4):164-74.
7. Dubinsky P, Boor A, Kincekova J, Tomasovicova O, Reiterova K, P B. Congenital trichinellosis? Case report. Parasite 2001;8((2 Suppl)):S180-2.
8. Mead P, Slutsker L, Dietz V, al e. Food-related illness and death in the United States. Emerg Infect Dis 1999;5:607-25.
9. Dubey J. Toxoplasmosis. J Am Vet Med Assoc 1994;205:1593-8.
10. Holliman R. Congenital toxoplasmosis: prevention, screening and treatment. J Hosp Infect 1995;30(suppl):179-90.

11. Carter A, Frank J. Congenital toxoplasmosis: epidemiologic features and control. CMAJ 1986;135:618-23.
12. Frenkel J. Prevention of toxoplasmosis during pregnancy: hygienic measures and vaccination. In: Carvajal H, Frenkel J, de Sanchez N, eds. Proceedings of the 1998 Bogota Toxoplasmosis. Bogota, Colombia: University of Los Andes, Sante Fe, 1998.
13. Reports Ra. Preventing Congenital Toxoplasmosis. MMWR Surveill Summ 2003;49(RR02):57-75.
14. Dimes Mo. Maternal, Infant, and Child Health in the United States. March of Dimes 2003 Data Book for Policy Makers, 2003.

POISON-ANIMAL & DISUNITY

Ways of the Poison-Animal

Key Terms: anterior cingulated cortex, chattel slavery, cognition, dementia, epilepsy, etiopathogenesis, genetically-manufactured, hormones, musculoskeletal, neocortical, neurocysticercosis, neurons, neurotransmitter, paranoia, parasites, pathogens, persecution syndrome, posterior cingulated cortex, Reconstruction Period, schizophrenia, subcortical, Taenium solium, Toxoplasma gondii

A popular criticism among Black people, which is usually hurled in the form of a cliché, is that we are like crabs in a barrel. Others say *bushel*. Still others say *bucket*. In all cases, creatures placed in bushels or barrels will act to pull each other down, especially when such creatures have large claws and are held captive. Crabs do not act this way in their natural environment. The ocean offers plenty of room for each one to do its own thing.

A more universal cliché is "You are what you eat". If we meld the two clichés, then we can surmise that some Black people act like crabs because they eat crabs. These persons may have a crab-like mentality, which is to scavenge. The barrel in this case could be the extremely limited opportunities offered through racist social systems that have many of us competing over the few available morsels at the expense of our own Brothers or Sisters. This, of course, is not natural behavior — nor are these systems established on the nature of human life, which is freedom, justice, equality, and the unlimited pursuit of happiness.

The point of this is that few of us connect our diet to how we act, yet we are affected in many ways by the foods and beverages we consume. With so many people, especially children, taking all sorts of narcotics to alter their behavior, most of us can identify with the effect that these drugs have on the mind. Those of us who have used drugs socially, or have consumed alcoholic beverages, are very knowledgeable of the array of moods and mental disorientation that result. We usually use these mind-altering substances to perceive our environment differently — *getting high* to *get away*. We are also prone to become physically and verbally abusive while in these demented mental states. Our perceptions are inaccurate.

CHEMICALS & BEHAVIOR
∎ ∎

Both legal and illegal drugs interface with the body's chemical messengers – hormones, neurons, etc. – and render a profound effect on the person's behavior. So, a child that is excited about life becomes subdued and disinterested after taking a mind-altering drug, which supposedly "calms" him or her down, making that child able to sit still in class. Where are the drugs that can "rev up" the curriculum rather than suppress the child?

Also, there are drugs for other ailments that alter brain function, and subsequently, the patient's behavior. For example, drugs that allegedly treat thyroid conditions often affect the person's brain. Drugs earmarked for sexual malfunction, obesity, diabetes, and heart disease often cause mental upset. So, whether the drug is destined for the brain or some other organ, it eventually has some level of impact on the brain.

Those who are familiar with how the human body operates know this to be true. Many others may not know much about this; and as a result, believe that the effect of a pill is confined to the area it supposedly treats. This has never been the case and scientific research has never confirmed this to be so. The so-called side effects associated with medications are the negative reactions these drugs have on other organs, as well as the immune system.

The body is a single entity, with circulatory and neuronal networks that connect all tissues and organs. Therefore, all drugs affect other organs in the body. This is similar to the way pathogens travel these biological networks and gain access to every organ in the poison-animal eater's body, including the brain. If parasites can navigate these networks as living organisms, how much easier can chemicals travel throughout these networks, particularly when drugs directly enter the bloodstream?

This applies to food, as food is comprised of chemicals, such as carbon, oxygen, nitrogen — which build amino acids, carbohydrates, and fats. The body degrades the food to these essential nutrients. Therefore, everything we eat or drink delivers some effect on the body, especially the brain. So, in reality, *we are what we eat*. This is not merely a cliche'. If people knew just how absolutely true this is, they would be more careful about what they eat. If people knew that they could take on the behavior of the creature or animal they eat, they would be extra cautious when selecting foods to eat.

Furthermore, if people knew that they could begin to look like the animals they eat, they would be especially careful about what they eat. This might inspire people to be more interested in learning how poison-animal actually looks and acts rather than settling for the cartoon characterizations of this animal — which are nowhere near the reality of this poisonous and genetically-manufactured beast.

The Honorable Elijah Muhammad calls our attention to those persons who have eaten so much poison-animal that they look like a human version of this animal. Poison-animal eaters' faces and bodies become drastically disfigured; confirming the reality that poison-animal destroys the eater's beauty appearance.

This loss of beauty is not just on the surface, which is the first to be ruined, but also in the distortion of physiological symmetry of the body. The body becomes acutely deformed, resembling that of the poison-animal. The poison-animal is a physically ugly looking thing. Nothing about this animal is beautiful or attractive, and eating this flesh makes the eater unattractive.

Additionally, the poison-animal eaters' ways and actions are like the poison-animal. This represents the quintessential loss of beauty — the inner beauty, which is representative of one's presence or aura.

Taking on the characteristics of an animal that is shameless, belligerent, and exceptionally foul, gives the poison-animal eater a potential ugliness that is not meant to be in the realm of human behavior.

In the civilized world, poison-animal eaters are disdained because of the foul disposition they usually exude. The human qualities that make people personable and a joy to be around are buried under the rubbish of rebellion against God and diseases from pathogens. The human body is not meant to harbor despicable pathogens that bring about disease and ugliness.

Considering these levels of ugliness is a difficult reality to confront, as we may know family members who are possessed of the poison-animal's looks and behaviors, but this is a reality in Black America and elsewhere. A great blessing is that this can be turned around for the better once poison-animal is forsaken from our diets.

PILLARS OF CONTROL
▪ ▪

With this as the backdrop, we can reason that our behavior is dictated or influenced by the foods we eat. It is also influenced by what we think – hence the proverb, "*As a man thinketh, so then is he*." If we think that we are nothing, then everything we touch will turn into salt. This means that those who control what we eat and what we think, control us. It is that simple.

As an enslaved and conquered people, Black people of America have been completely controlled through food and knowledge. Many historians cite the awesome control the slave masters had over the lives of enslaved Black people — men, women and children. The power they exercised over us was comprehensive.

The Caucasian enslavers controlled every aspect of our lives. They decided when we ate and what we ate; when we slept and where we slept; when we worked, where we worked, and how long we worked; when we bathed, where we bathed, and how we bathed; when we mated and with whom we mated; when we talked and how we talked;

when we walked, where we walked, and even how we walked; when we cried and laughed; and when we danced and sang. We existed at their leisure. We lived or died at their pleasure. This is historical fact, and much of this control remains even today.

In Chapter 1, we took up the issue of how poison-animal entered Black America's diet and the fact that the Medical Profession knew that eating poison-animal destroyed the mind and beauty appearance of the eater. Yet, this poison meat was purposely fed to Black people, and then medically justified as a healthy food to feed those enslaved.

After the post-slavery period, this poison meat was glorified among us, becoming highly touted as "soul food". Our enemies still considered this meat as "kill the soul" food. How then did we arrive at the opposite view of the slave diet? Perhaps, we began branding the poison-animal as soul food when we were allowed to "cut-the-fool", with a pig foot in our hands, at the weekend speakeasies, shortly following the Reconstruction Period.

Poison-animal became the featured "party hardy" meat. This meat, along with liquor, soul music and dance, comprised the so-called *soulful* environment, which is actually an outgrowth of our chattel slavery experience, and brings about similar socially unhealthy consequences.

In Chapter 7, we also dealt with how poison-animal *sounds* the mental power. To reiterate, parasites invade the brain, interrupting the circuitry that serves as the foundation for our ability to think and act properly. The brain tissues and cells are destroyed. In the end, an array of physically destructive activities ensues — from brain swelling to brain cancer. So, the poison-animal eater is robbed of his or her ability to understand the simple truths and laws of life, such as "cause and effect"; "seek and ye shall find"; "knock and the door shall be opened"; and, "eat to live, not live to eat." Overall, the ability to plan and calculate is destroyed.

A mere observance of the great financial wealth funneled through the hands of Black America, and the pitiful outcomes of this wealth, confirms that something is deficient in our collective brain power. We are a people upon whom other peoples become wealthy, yet we remain impoverished. Therefore, our poverty is our inability to think and act logically on behalf of ourselves. Our poverty is also our inability to unite. This leads to the essential aim of this chapter — how eating poison-animal thwarts our disunity.

MENINGEAL ARTERY, MIDDLE, SAGITTAL SECTION

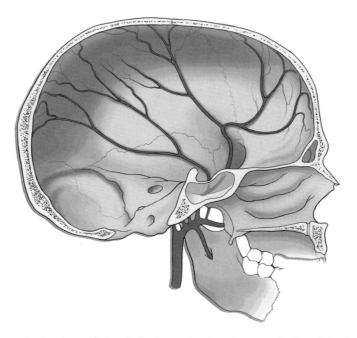

Poison-animal pathogens infect the brain, causing disturbances to the flow of blood and brain fluid. Conditions such as schizophrenia and epilepsy result. This leads to reduced cognition and mental retardation develops.

UNITY IS NATURAL

As social beings and as a nation within a nation, unity among Black people should be a natural outgrowth. Our unity should be just as natural as breathing. Therefore, if we are not enjoying unity, it means that unnatural ploys are being used to frustrate, impede, and destroy our ability and willingness to unite. This is precisely the case, and history bears witness to this. Both the Honorable Elijah Muhammad and the Honorable Minister Louis Farrakhan have taught extensively on this issue.

This ploy comprises control over what we eat and what we think. Black people's open enemies have executed this evil through a diet of poison-animal, coupled with a teaching that infuses inferiority, low self-esteem, and self-hatred. This has made us crablike. It has literally made many of us "poison-animal" in thought and action.

Certainly, if the poison-animal pathogens that infest the brain cause mental disability and retardation, how reasonable is it that the eater's behavior is altered, as well; making him or her disagreeable to interact with, in peace and harmony, to achieve noble aims.

The Honorable Elijah Muhammad writes:

> The poisonous hog flesh makes the color of many people's eyes muddy and reddish in appearance and makes the people who eat it brazen, careless, easy to anger, fight and oppose each other.

These words reveal the fact that the poison-animal eater is possessed of the poison-animal's looks, and foul and nasty spirit. Not only has the person acquired the dangerous pathogens harbored in this beast, but also they have taken on the animal's destructive spirit, which result from disruptions to their neurological processes.

There is also the element of "energies", which is a dimension not very well understood or discussed by mainstream scientists. However, its consideration is demonstrated in how the people of God are required to slaughter animals when taking them as food. The life of the animal should not be taken while the animal is in a state of fear for its life.

Fear has an extraordinary and encompassing impact on the animal, including the state of its flesh, which reflects the energies of the animal at slaughter time. When we consume this flesh, it becomes a part of us, producing the opposite results of what our intentions were for eating this flesh. Our purpose for eating it was to gain nourishment, but the manner through which it was killed has made it highly toxic. Eating this toxic flesh has an adverse affect on our health, and naturally so.

We consume the spirit of the animal, in the form of molecular structures and other energies. This is partly why the Honorable

Elijah Muhammad teaches that no meat is good for human consumption. Not only is meat hard on the digestive system, but also the spirit of the animal has a bearing on the eater's health.

There is much to this subject; however, the point is that eating the flesh of poison-animal brings the spirit of this beast into the life force of the eater. This point cannot be emphasized enough — *we are what we eat*.

This subject sheds light on the awesomeness of divine guidance and why we must follow it. Clearly, this world does not know, nor do those who run it care to know about the richness of creation. Everything associated with *this world* is materially superficial. It is a world of sport, play, vanity, and an inordinate pursuit of profit for destructive purposes.

The richness of divine guidance is exemplified in the multidimensional states of our existence and how each has a critical role in the quality of our lives, including how long we live. Methuselah and Noah lived nearly a thousand years because they understood the nature of things. Most of us cannot imagine these great prophets of God, including Jesus, eating a bowl of chitterlings, yet many people who claim righteousness, eat this divinely-forbidden flesh.

POISON-ANIMAL CHARACTERISTICS

Let us now examine the words of the Honorable Elijah Muhammad regarding the following traits of the poison-animal eater: *brazen* and *careless.*

There are many synonyms for *brazen*:

Brash, unabashed, unashamed, shameless, blatant, garish, loud, meretricious, obtrusive, tasteless, vulgar, crude, feisty, confrontational, insulting and offensive.

When considering these words, attention is drawn as to why the poison-animal must possess these characteristics. Again, if we are what we eat, we should want to know the details about the nature of the food, in this case, the animal we are eating.

In addition to serving as a medicine, poison-animal also served as a live waste disposal. It is still used in this way, today. Many small farms feed poison-animal swill, which is garbage and waste.

The poison-animal had the chore of cleaning up the filth in Europe, where the Caucasian people dwelled in caves for approximately two thousand years after being banished from the civilized world. The knowledge of this history, as given to us by Master Fard Muhammad, described how they plunged into savagery and followed the ways of the animals and beasts that lived among them. This was due to their lack of divine guidance.

The Prophet Moses was assigned to resurrect Caucasian people from their cave-like and completely savage condition. Moses was assigned to teach the Caucasian people how to live respectful lives and build homes for themselves. He also gave them a teaching that showed them how to use extreme trickery to become a dominant people. Since the Coming of Master Fard Muhammad, we have become more aware of the kinds of tricks they use, and do not fall for them as we once did.

This history gives us a deep sense of the workings of Almighty God in sending messengers and prophets to humanity. Prophets are not sent to write hymns and organize choirs. They are sent to address the needs of the people to whom they are sent. Therefore, Caucasian people needed houses because living in caves, mountainsides, and treetops were not suitable for humans.

Caucasian people also needed to learn how to cook their food, care for themselves, and in general, learn the ways of the civilized world, so that they could be fit to come out of Europe and interact with the civilized world.

It stands to reason that houses could not have been successfully built until the ghastly grime of both animal and human carcasses, human and animal feces, human and animal waste, and the overall grotesque conditions of Europe were remedied. This was a foremost problem — how to get rid of and manage extremely high volumes of filth that made Europe a total waste dump.

One of the remedies was the genetically-manufactured poison-animal. This was covered in Chapter 2. The Arab scientists charged with making poison-animal combined the genetic material of the cat, rat and dog to produce this distinct animal. In making this beast, the scientists had to keep the animal's mission in mind.

What would an animal having such an assignment need to possess? Of course, it must have an affinity for filth, with no discernment of good or bad — *unabashed, unashamed,* and *shameless.* It must have no regard for what it ate, how it ate, and where it ate — *vulgar, crude, tasteless* and *obtrusive.* It would need an aggressive spirit because time is not a luxury — *brazen, blatant, and loud.* Therefore, it would need a staunch sense of purpose to carve out and secure its feeding territory, regardless of whom or what — *feisty, confrontational, insulting* and *offensive.*

POISON-ANIMAL

The purpose and mission of the poison-animal speaks to the type of characteristics is must possess.

A careful study of the poison-animal substantiates all of this. In addition, awareness of the cantankerous nature of poison-animal sheds light on the animal's internal turmoil caused by the conflicting natures of the animals – cat, rat, and dog – that comprise its genetic makeup. These animals are natural opponents, and each has unique abilities.

Only the people familiar with handling or looking upon this beast know this to be true. The multitude of others have cartoon characterizations of this animal as their frame of reference, which is among the greatest deceptions perpetrated in the history of mankind.

No doubt, in order to complete the monumental assignment of serving as a live garbage disposal, the poison-animal would have to be *"careless"* about its health, as well as the health of anything else. The Honorable Elijah Muhammad notes that this animal is so dumb that it does not seek shelter from thunder and lightening, opting to continue to eat. This is carelessness of a suicidal sort. Synonyms for careless include:

> Heedless, thoughtless, uncaring, neglectful, negligent, oblivious, inattentive, irresponsible, incautious, and wild.

POISON-ANIMAL EATER IN ACTION

The United States social environment features pandemics of emergency hospital visits for gunshot and stab wounds, fist-fights and an array of other mental and physical assaults that are in keeping with the ways of the poison-animal. American cities and "hoods" are overwhelmed by robberies, thievery, rapes, drug dealing, substance abuse and brazen acts of disrespect and disregard for human life, which are all consistent with the ways of the poison-animal.

The social scourges of substance abuse, teen pregnancy, incest, disrespect of children and family ties, and the unresponsiveness in caring for the children we bring into the world are pandemic in Black America and throughout the world. Although many of us know better, many of us do not do better. We perpetuate this extremely painful way of living, while knowing the end results. Again, these are the actions of the poison-animal.

These inhumane traits are further exacerbated by ignorant philosophies we take as wisdom, such as *"I got mine, you got yours to get"*. Generally, the thought to build a future for our children is not totally established in our thinking. This is selfishness of the highest order. These are the ways of the poison-animal.

Considering all of the above, if we checked the homes of such persons, we would find poison-animal meat. We would find that poison-animal is a major item in our diets. This was substantiated in Chapter 1, where, according to the USDA, each Black person in America eats approximately 63 pounds of poison-animal annually. Of course, there are many who do not eat poison-animal, but these persons are the exception. The rule is that poison-animal is in Black America's diet in a big way.

POISON-ANIMAL & BEHAVIORAL RESEARCH

Studies that assessed how parasitic infections affect a person's behavior support the Honorable Elijah Muhammad's words regarding the overall inability of the poison-animal eater to function as a representative of the civilized world. For example, a study titled, *Clinical Aspects, Diagnosis and Treatment of Trichinellosis* described the following:[1]

> In people with severe trichinellosis, blurring of consciousness or excessive excitation, as well as somnolence and apathy, have been observed.

Somnolence is a state of drowsiness or sleepiness. It is a condition of semi-consciousness, approaching comatose. This validates what is mentioned in *Problem 9* of the *Problem Book*, wherein the poison-animal eater's brain is sounded or deaden. Naturally, such a condition is akin to apathy, as persons suffering brain damage are prone to lack interest or concern in matters of importance. They display indifference and the lack of emotion or feeling.

The Honorable Minister Louis Farrakhan has called attention to Black America's lack of apathy or feelings for each other — that is, if a Black person is dealt an injustice in Alabama, we should feel it in Pennsylvania; and if we do not, then we are disconnected. Part of this disconnection is the brain damage caused by poison-animal pathogens. The other part is attributed to the training in self-hatred we received over the past four centuries.

According to several definitions, *excitation* is:

> The state of being emotionally aroused or worked up; the neural or electrical arousal of an organ or muscle or gland; and something that agitates and arouses.

The poison-animal eater experiences agitation, as he or she is easy to anger, fight and oppose other people. This is what makes the person brazen and difficult to get along with in peace. This condition, as with the others, is the result of brain malfunction caused by parasitic infections, ignorance and miseducation.

Another study examined the health conditions of patients many years after battling acute parasitic infections.[2] The researcher describing this study stated:[1]

> Nonetheless, there have been reports of people who, months or even years after the acute stage, continued to suffer from chronic pain, general discomfort, tingling, numbness and excessive sweating, and who showed signs of paranoia and a syndrome of persecution.

Paranoia and persecution syndrome are psychotic conditions associated with schizophrenia. According to several definitions, *schizophrenia* is:

> A severe brain disease that interferes with normal brain and mental function — it can trigger hallucinations, delusions, paranoia, and significant lack of motivation.

Health authorities assert that there is no definitive cause of schizophrenia. This means that scientists have not been able to pinpoint a specific or single cause for this condition. Who says that it has to be a single cause? In a world driven by greed and the disrespect of human life, there are many avenues through which our brains can be damaged — eating diseased meat happens to be a major one.

Since 1953, numerous studies have confirmed the connection between *Toxoplasma gondii* (T. gondii) infection and schizophrenia and other severe psychiatric disorders. Some medications used to treat schizophrenia were found effective against T. gondii parasites.

POISON-ANIMAL SUFFERING DEPRESSION

As a repository for many brain-destroying parasites and viruses, poison-animal is known to suffer severe mental diseases.

There is also a known link between epilepsy and schizophrenia or schizophrenia-like psychosis. Researchers suggest that the two conditions *may share common genetic or environmental causes.*[3] According to these findings, people with epilepsy had approximately three times the risk of schizophrenia than the general population. As previously stated, brain parasites, such as T. gondii and *Taenium solium* are leading causes of epilepsy. Both parasites are also leading causes of schizophrenia. Many other pathogens that infect the brain also cause these ailments.

Theories that link infectious agents, such as parasites, to mental diseases, especially schizophrenia, date back to the late 1800s.[4] In 1896, the Scientific American journal published an article titled, *Is Insanity Due To A Microbe?* In the early part of the 20th century, theories that linked diseases to parasites dominated medical thought. This view later fizzed out. It died out along with its proponents — who were far more intelligent and sincere than the medical practitioners that govern today's trillion dollar healthcare industry.

The concern that parasitic infections are linked to common chronic diseases has heightened over the past few decades. This concern, of course, is confined to the scientific community, as the average citizen is unaware of the emergence of parasitic infections, as well as the popular diseases these infections cause. However, studies on this matter are becoming commonplace.

In one study, researchers set out to examine the relationship between schizophrenia and parasitic infections. The aim was to determine the frequency and features of psychiatric morbidity with neurocysticercosis, the condition caused by the brain parasite, T. gondii.[5] The study featured 38 outpatients who were examined and, subsequently, diagnosed with schizophrenic psychiatric diseases and cognitive decline. These conditions were found in 65.8 and 87.5 percent of the cases, respectively.

The term *cognition* refers to mental functions, such as the ability to think, reason, and remember. It is defined:

> The conscious process of knowing or being aware of thoughts or perceptions, including understanding and reasoning.

Cognition also represents high level functions carried out by the human brain, including:

> Comprehension and use of speech, visual perception and construction, calculation ability, attention (information processing), memory, and executive functions such as planning, problem-solving, and self-monitoring.

Diminished cognition reduces a person's quality of life. The losses of these mental functions provide additional support of how a person can be effectively robbed of wealth and life. In fact, the only wealth each of us really has is the life that the Creator has given us. When evil people can use our lives for their good fortune, we have been thoroughly robbed.

According to this study, depression was the most frequent psychiatric diagnosis, affecting approximately 53 percent of the patients. About 14 percent of the patients were deemed psychotic. The findings indicate that psychiatric abnormalities, particularly depression syndromes, occur frequently in patients with neurocysticercosis, and that:

> Although regarded as a rare cause of dementia, mild cognitive impairment may be a much more prevalent neuropsychological feature of patients with neurocysticercosis.

This means that anyone having neurocysticercosis experiences mental impairment, with acute dementia being the most pronounced indicator. With nearly a third of the world's population infected with brain parasites, mild cognitive impairment is pandemic. Taking this a step further — anyone who has eaten poison-animal is infected with the parasite that causes neurocysticercosis.

Dementia is also pandemic. This mental condition is generally described:

> The profound and progressive loss of intellectual function, sometimes associated with personality change, which results from loss of brain substance, and is sufficient to interfere with a person's normal, functional activities.

People suffering dementia are unable to properly perceive and interpret their immediate surroundings, and consequently, they make mistakes in judgment. According to the study, brain lesions were responsible for the mental changes.

Health researchers in another study investigated the levels of antibodies of infectious agents in the serum and cerebral spinal fluid (CSF) of individuals with recent onset schizophrenia.[6] They found that untreated individuals with recent onset schizophrenia had significantly increased levels of serum and *CSF IgG* antibodies for *cytomegalovirus* and T. gondii. Cytomegalovirus is a member of the herpesvirus family. Therefore, these people were infected by parasites and viruses — both causing brain damage.

The findings of this study pinpointed the role of infectious agents, such as parasites and viruses, in the *etiopathogenesis* of schizophrenia.

Another study opened with this same outlook:[7]

> Recent epidemiologic studies indicate that infectious agents may contribute to some cases of schizophrenia. In animals, infections with Toxoplasma gondii can alter behavior and neurotransmitter function. In humans, acute infection with T. gondii can produce psychotic symptoms similar to those displayed by persons with schizophrenia.

Researchers of this study recommended that establishing the role of this parasite in the etiopathogenesis of schizophrenia could lead to new medications for prevention and treatment. Of course, the best prevention is stay away from both foods and activities that can cause these infections.

The prevalence of intestinal parasitic infection among institutionalized and non-institutionalized people with mental handicaps in Thailand was assessed.[8] Researchers found that the rate of infection was much higher in institutionalized (57.6%) than in non-institutionalized people (7.5%). Many parasites were found in institutionalized mental patients. These included Trichuris trichiura (29.7%), Entamoeba coli (23.1%), Giardia intestinalis (8.0%), Hymenolepis nana (7.8%), and Entamoeba histolytica/dispar (7.1%).

The findings suggest that:

> Institutionalized mentally handicapped people should be considered a high-risk group for intestinal parasitic infection and parasitic control measures should be emphasized.

These parasites are the cause for the institutionalization of these people. In Chapter 5, we noted that an estimated 600 cases of trichinosis are reported annually in just one Thailand province, alone, not to mention the entire country.[9] The *careless* diets of many people living in Asian countries have made these places havens for parasitic diseases.

In Black communities, Asian eateries thrive, and Black people who eat this food believe they are eating novel foods. However, included in these foods are a host of novel parasites and other dangerous pathogens. With such stores selling poison-animal galore, there is not any wonder why the health crisis in Black America is at an all-time high.

Another study that examined more than 500 mentally retarded patients in an Italian mental institution, found that nearly 25 percent were infected with intestinal parasites.[10] The infections were most frequent in young men, those with severe mental retardation, the chronically institutionalized, and those living in older wards. A cross segment of the population was represented in these infections. This showed that parasites do not discriminate — men, women, children and the young and old are targets of pathogens.

Holistically, the overall affect of parasitic infestation of the brain is that it stifles and retards the person's mental development. This is a dire concern among health agencies battling parasitic infections in developing countries.[11] Infected children usually experience mental retardation that continues for the rest of their lives. Infected adults, on the other hand, regress to a childlike mentality. This, however, usually does not happen in dramatic fashion — the process is gradual.

There is gross evidence that adults are increasingly behaving like children. In fact, this is quite obvious. The nationwide display of impatience, rudeness, and social and domestic violence is among the many signs that life as we once knew it is descending into a bestiality that will soon resemble what Caucasians experienced in Europe over 4,000 years ago — a complete absence of civilization, and 100 percent rejection of anything divine and humane.

SEAT OF EMOTIONS AND PERCEPTION

The brain is not solely responsible for how we perceive our environment. Using the scenario of computer technology, the brain can be considered the hardware, and our experiences, knowledge and understanding of things can be considered the software. Together, the two determine how we perceive our environment and provide us with the foundation for effectively functioning within this environment.

Revisiting the definition of brain, it states:

> The portion of the vertebrate central nervous system that is enclosed within the cranium, continuous with the spinal cord, and composed of gray matter and white matter. It is also the seat of consciousness, thought, memory, and emotion.

As previously addressed, when the brain is injured, the person's ability to function is affected. Most of us may know persons who have permanent behavioral problems caused by some type of brain injury.

When the *gray matter* responsible for managing our perceptions and emotions is injured, a litany of emotional and behavior problems ensue. These can be mild or severe mental disorders. They can also be temporary or permanent.

Scientists have been seeking to learn about the areas of the brain that serve as the seat of consciousness, thought, memory and emotion. Many areas of the brain have been studied and some of these findings have been put forth. For example, some scientists suggest that the brain can reasonably be divided into two general regions: the *neocortical* and the *subcortical*.[12] The subcortical is deemed the part where emotions are generated through autonomic, neurotransmitter and neuroactive peptide, hormonal, and musculoskeletal systems.

Other studies have focused on the involvement of both right- and left-brain hemispheres in controlling our emotions. In the research paper, *"Neuroanatomical Correlates of Impaired Recognition of Emotion in Dementia"*, the authors state:[13]

> Several investigators have examined the relationship between emotional processing and lesions in the right and left hemispheres and demonstrated that certain aspects of emotional processing are dependent on the right hemisphere.

In addition to these broad segments of the brain, more isolated parts of the brain have been studied for potential roles in regulating certain emotions or behaviors. For example, the *amygdala* has long been considered a processor of emotions of fear and anger.[14]

Other researchers have suggested that the anterior cingulate cortex has a role in some manifestations of pain, happiness and empathy,[15] while the posterior cingulate cortex is purported to have some responsibility for emotions of sadness, disappointment and related emotions.[16] Various neurotransmitters, peptides, and hormones associated with the limbic system are also involved in the operation of these organs; and therefore, also have roles in controlling emotions and behavior.[17]

The effort to identify the areas of brain that process emotions is a challenging task. Moreover, the entire brain is a single organ and its circuitry, in concert with other organs and systems, are involved in how we perceive and interact with our environment. These studies, however, prove that the brain is the "hardware" through which our perceptions, emotions, and behaviors arise.

Again, it holds true that anyone who can manage the destruction of our brains by controlling what we eat and what we think has complete control over our perceptions and behaviors. Such a person or group of persons can direct us into acting out reckless or death-style behaviors, while making us perceive these actions as enjoyment.

SOCIAL ENGINEERING & POISON-ANIMAL

Here, we must note an additional element of control – social control – that bears on our subject. A 1984 study, *"Overpopulation Crisis"*, revealed findings about the violent response, on the part of animals, to conditions of crowding.[18] The study showed that when the population goes beyond a certain density, producing overcrowding, the social balance is disturbed. Consequently, the potential for "all hell to break loose" is high. In that state, violence is imminent.

With respect to familial duties, the researchers observed that the natural mammalian sensitivities of care and protection of offspring were transformed into behaviors of indifference, neglect, competition, domination, and ultimately, murder. We can assume that the climate of overcrowding made efforts to protect offspring extremely difficult, particularly in a predatory climate.

This study suggested that human communities weakened by crowding are more likely to succumb to certain stress diseases and to have less resilience against parasites.

However, the recommendations put forth were ludicrous and are expressed in the following:

> Given the power of modern military technology, it is imperative that human populations avert a population crisis response by substituting voluntary fertility control for involuntary mortality control.

The satanic spirit displayed through these words represent the mindset of this world. The "crafters" of this study ignored the fact that comparing humans to lower animals is like comparing apples to oranges, unless humans are diminished to animalistic levels. This has been done, particularly in Black communities designated as "the hood".

The earth is vast and most of us who have driven up and down major interstates know that there is plenty of undeveloped land; however, Black America is cooped up in isolated areas. This is evidence that the awesome control that Caucasian America had over Black people during the chattel slavery era persists. This control is for diabolical purposes; and this study substantiates their wicked intent.

Given this fact, it is imperative that we minimize and eventually eliminate predatory and animalistic behaviors, which continue to produce savage-like living conditions and experiences. Poison-animal consumption has a major role in keeping Black people anchored to these unproductive and inhumane conditions that breed violence, carelessness, disrespect and disunity. In spite of our enemy's social engineering, which places us at a disadvantage, a heightened intelligence will enable us to produce a better quality of life than what is currently being experienced.

AGAINST UNITY

Poison-animal is a disuniting force because it ravages the brain, which is the only organ responsible for human reasoning and the expression of divine love.

HINDRANCE OF REASONING

The Honorable Minister Louis Farrakhan described *reasoning* as the highest form of thinking or thought, which means that one's cognition must be at optimum levels. Reasoning is the act of using *reason* to form conclusions, inferences, and judgments. Reasoning is:

> Having the capacity for logical, rational, and analytic thought; intelligence; good judgment; sound sense; and a normal mental state.

Reasoning is sanity. The opposite of reasoning is insanity. *Insanity* is:

> A deranged state of the mind usually occurring as a specific disorder (as schizophrenia). It is also an unsoundness of mind or lack of understanding, as preventing the person from having the mental capacity required by law to enter into a particular relationship, status, or transaction.

For the sake of simplicity, we can view the brain damage caused by poison-animal pathogens as a means of preventing the poison-animal eater from mentally maturing to the extent that he or she can set destructive emotions aside and use the power of reasoning to arrive at constructive and positive solutions and conclusions. As indicated throughout this chapter, the brain damage levied by pathogens causes the poison-animal eater to experience delusions that feature paranoia and persecution syndromes.

This deranged mental state fosters destructive attitudes and behaviors that lead to evil and diabolical actions. Jealousy and envy are among the most destructive, and represent the ultimate mental derangement and misperception of reality.

There is absolutely no way that unity can be forged among persons subdued by these mental states. Acts such as fighting, backbiting, arguing, betrayal, and treachery are to be expected. Such persons are easily offended, rejecting helpful criticism and desiring to harm those who disagree with them about any matter. They become intensely disagreeable, and because they view differences of opinion as personal attacks, they hold grudges for life. A "snowball in hell" stands a better chance of surviving than creating unity among persons of this mindset and character.

The damaged brain anchors the poison-animal eater to childlike outlooks, attitudes and behaviors. The resulting characteristics are similar to what was previously described; however, childlike or immature behaviors are more selfish and emotionally driven.

Watching elementary school children in action sheds light on how adults act under the weight of neurological damage. Selfishness, envy, jealously, uncontrolled desires for superficial thrills, and an overall disposition of folly are facets of this level of immaturity.

A child's mental state is commensurable with its physical development, and his or her actions are controlled by the parents, thus limiting the social harm. However, at the adult stage, this unfettered deranged mental state can cause widespread destruction.

The Scriptures informs us of the mindset of people living in the Last Days. In *2 Timothy 3:2-5*, it reads:

> People will be lovers of themselves, lovers of money, boastful, proud, abusive, disobedient to their parents, ungrateful, unholy, without love, unforgiving, slanderous, without self-control, brutal, not lovers of the good, treacherous, rash, conceited, lovers of pleasure rather than lovers of God – having a form of godliness but denying its power.

The mass marketing of poison-animal, which has made this diseased meat widely consumed across the globe, is intrinsically involved in the current fulfillment of this prophecy. The consumption of poison-animal is a key strategy used by the rulers of this world to keep people divided and steeped in these prophetic scourges.

Again, such persons under this curse include those who claim to know and love Almighty God. Great preaching and singing do not prevent the poison-animal pathogens from destroying the brain. Besides, eating this diseased animal is against divine law.

HINDRANCE OF DIVINE LOVE

The expression of love is the fuel that forges unity. The description of love given by this world is mere folly and lust, having no permanency. This word *love* is hurled throughout movies and songs that depict sin, lust, indecency, and disrespect of human life. Again, we turn to the Scriptures for the correct description of love. In *1 Corinthians 13:4*, it states:

> Love is patient, love is kind. It does not envy, it does not boast, it is not proud.

These traits or attributes are diametrically opposed to the behaviors that result from eating poison-animal. This diseased flesh alters the eater's mind, consequently, interfering with the person's ability to resurrect the human qualities that promote love and unity within self, and among the civilized world.

By eating poison-animal, the eater is burying and destroying divine qualities and virtues, such as patience, tolerance, humility, modesty, an inclination to trust, positive thinking, and a general willingness to cooperate and participate in activities rooted in goodness and divinity.

Although unity among humans is designed to be a natural experience and is our birthright as social beings, it is not achieved without challenges and obstacles. Among the things that make it challenging is our individual growth in divinity. This, the Honorable Elijah Muhammad teaches, is among the most difficult to recognize and develop. This is also what it means to be resurrected — as we are resurrected into the character of God. This world makes our pursuit of divinity an uphill road, and millions of people never take the first step towards this goal. In fact, we can safely say that most people never consider it a goal.

There are many people that – without having parasitic infections in their brains – do not see humans as being of the divine or having divine potential, although both the Bible and Holy Quran make it clear that this is our ultimate purpose in life. Divinity is established on the character of Almighty God. Everything that HE is, we are required to strive to become.

This divine character, combined with our ability to reason, enables Black America to secure perpetual unity, particularly unity involving our forward march to higher expressions of life. The enormity of our problems is such that each of us must *rise above emotion into the thinking of God*. This cannot be achieved as long as we allow ourselves to be destroyed by the pathogens harbored in poison-animal; and incur Almighty God's disfavor by breaking divine law.

PREREQUISITES FOR UNITY

Obeying the divine laws given to the prophets, particularly Moses and Muhammad (peace be upon these worthy servants of God) are prerequisites for our ascension in the resurrection process governed by Master Fard Muhammad through HIS Chief Servants, the Honorable Elijah Muhammad and the Honorable Minister Louis Farrakhan. Both men have exhorted us to obey the divine laws mentioned throughout the Scriptures.

The need to get from under the diabolical control of satanic rulership sheds great light on the value of the LIFE Almighty God, in the Person of Master Fard Muhammad, gave to the Honorable Elijah Muhammad to give to Black people of America — as the means of transforming our lives from subhuman levels to the divine character of God. This LIFE is in accordance with our nature. This LIFE is our nature. Accepting this LIFE is a dire requirement if we are to be resurrected as a people.

The following words from the Honorable Elijah Muhammad are found on page 179, in *How To Eat To Live, Book 2*:

> HOW TO EAT TO LIVE is one of the number two Blessings that Allah (God) Who Came in the Person of Master Fard Muhammad To Whom Praises are due forever Has Brought to us.

The other "Blessing" is the body of knowledge for our spiritual and moral development — the knowledge of the reality of God, self, others, and the time in which we live. These two Blessings, when accepted by each of us, allows Almighty God to recapture control of our lives, as these bodies of knowledge govern how we eat and how we think. Both Blessings, however, are orchestrated through HIS divine servants for our benefit.

This is in keeping with the Way of God, in that HE deposits HIS revelation in a messenger, who serves as an example of how best to apply HIS knowledge and wisdom in our lives.

Finally, we must remember that the prophets and messengers of Almighty God forbade the eating and touching of poison-animal. We are required to obey divine law for the sake of our health and lives.

REFERENCES

1. Pozio E, Gomez Morales M, Dupouy-Camet J. Clinical aspects, diagnosis and treatment of trichinellosis. Expert Rev Anti Infect Ther 2003;1(3):471-82.

2. Pielok L. Clinical analysis and evaluation of selected laboratory parameters in patients examined in distant periods after trichinellosis. Wiad Parazytol 2001;47:185-209.

3. Qin P, Xu H, Laursen TM, Vestergaard M, Mortensen PB. Risk for schizophrenia and schizophrenia-like psychosis among patients with epilepsy: population based cohort study. BMJ 2005;331(7507):23-.

4. Torrey E, Yolken R. The Schizophrenia–Rheumatoid Arthritis Connection: Infectious, Immune, or Both? Brain Behav Immun 2001;15(4):401-410.

5. Forlenza O, Filho A, Nobrega J, dos Ramos Machado L, de Barros N, de Camargo C, da Silva M. Psychiatric manifestations of neurocysticercosis: a study of 38 patients from a neurology clinic in Brazil. Neurol Neurosurg Psychiatry 1997;62(6):612-616.

6. Leweke FM, Gerth C, Koethe D, KlosterkÐ¹tter J, Ruslanova I, Krivogorsky B, Torrey EF, Yolken R. Antibodies to infectious agents in individuals with recent onset schizophrenia. European Archives of Psychiatry and Clinical Neuroscience 2004;254(1):4-8.

7. Torrey E, Yolken R. Toxoplasma gondii and schizophrenia. Emerg Infect Dis. 2003;9(11):1375-80.

8. Sirivichayakul C, Pojjaroen-anant C, Wisetsing P, Siripanth C, Chanthavanich P, Pengsaa K. Prevalence of intestinal parasitic infection among Thai people with mental handicaps. Southeast Asian J Trop Med Public Health 2003;34(2):259-63.

9. Liu M, Boireau P. Trichinellosis in China: epidemiology and control. Trends Parasitol 2002;18:553-556.

10. Gatti S, Lopes R, Cevini C, Ijaoba B, Bruno A, Bernuzzi A, de Lio P, Monco A, Scaglia M. Intestinal parasitic infections in an institution for the mentally retarded. Ann Trop Med Parasitol 2000;94(5):453-60.

11. Moller A. A review of developmental instability, parasitism and disease Infection, genetics and evolution. Infect Genet Evol 2005;[Epub ahead of print].

12. Turner J, Stets J. The Sociology of Emotions. Boston, MA: Cambridge University Press, 2005.

13. Rosen H, Wilson M, chauer G, Allison S, Gorno-Tempini M, Pace-Savitsky C, Kramer J, Levenson R, Weiner M, Miller B. Neuroanatomical correlates of impaired recognition of emotion in dementia. Neuropsychologia 2005.

14. Phelps E, Ledoux J. Contributions of the Amygdala to Emotion Processing: From Animal Models to Human Behavior. Neuron 2005;48(2):175-187.

15. Shibasaki H. Central mechanisms of pain perception. Suppl Clin Neurophysiol 2004;57:39-49.

16. Aleman A. Feelings you can't imagine: towards a cognitive neuroscience of alexithymia. Trends Cogn Sci 2005.

17. Vianna M, Coitinho A, Izquierdo I. Role of the hippocampus and amygdala in the extinction of fear-motivated learning. Curr Neurovasc Res 2004;1(1):55-60.

18. Russell C, Russell W. Overpopulation crisis. Soc Biol Hum Aff 1984;49(1):23-42.

INDEX

migratory phase 85
neurological damage 91
nurse-cell formation 49, 65
persists after host death 71
reemerging parasite 50, 52
respiratory damage 89
various species 52
Trichinosis
chronic infection 95
clinical pathologies 80
global prevalence 71
prevention 73

U
USDA
cooking recommendations for
swine 73

PERILS OF EATING POISON-ANIMAL